CORRIGENDA

Page 32
Catalogue number 4, "The illustration, Fig.5"
should read, "The illustration, Fig.9"

Page 52
Catalogue number 67, "See Fig.6"
should read, "See Fig.10"

Page 53
Catalogue number 69, "(Fig.7)" and "(see Fig.7)"
should read, "(Fig.11)" and "(see Fig.11)"

Page 56
Catalogue number 70, "(Fig.8)" should read, "(Fig.12)"
and "See Fig.9" should read, "See Fig.13"

KLAYA-HO-ALTH

("Welcome" in Nuu-chah-nulth)

Collections from the Northwest Coast of North America
in the Royal Albert Memorial Museum, Exeter

Text and illustrations: Jane Burkinshaw

Published in 1999 with grant aid from the Heritage Lottery Fund

© Exeter City Museums

ISBN: 1 - 85522 - 695 - 2

Dedicated to the memory of my father, Eric Burkinshaw, 1924 - 1998.

The front cover photograph is of Ilchinik, the Nuu-chah-nulth totem pole
(catalogue number 79) carved for Exeter in 1998 by master carver
Tim Paul, senior carvers Patrick Amos, Francis Mark, and Leslie Mickey,
and apprentice carvers Corey Baiden and Tom Paul.

Back cover photograph:
Members of the Na-yii-i family of the Nuu-chah-nulth nation
with Ilchinik on the first day of the Totem Pole Project at
Exeter Museum, June 1998.

Photography (unless otherwise stated): David Garner 01395 568977
Designed and produced by Steelhead Limited 01392 432189

Contents

Painting the carved totem pole, Ilchinik (number 79), June 1998.

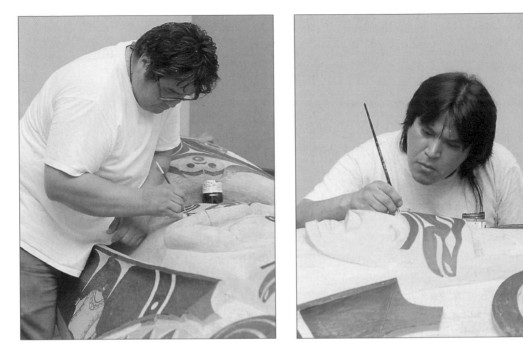

1. Master carver, Tim Paul.

2. Senior carver, Patrick Amos.

3. Tim Paul with the author and John Sealey, film-maker.

PREFACE

T he purpose of this catalogue is to show the full range of the collections held by Exeter City Museums that originate from First Nations artists and artisans on the Northwest Coast of North America.

This Museum has one of the finest provincial collections of Northwest Coast artefacts in Britain. They include objects from the voyages of Captains James Cook and George Vancouver which have received scholarly attention since the late 1970s. These pieces first came to the notice of a wider audience when items from the Vancouver, Agassiz, Ross and Devon and Exeter Institution collections were exhibited at the Seattle World's Fair in 1962.

The Vancouver collections were exhibited more recently, on both occasions at Vancouver Museum: in 1978 to mark the bicentenary of the arrival of Captain Cook at Nootka Sound and in 1986 during the city of Vancouver's Centennial celebrations.

The items from the Cook and Vancouver voyages in these collections are well known among those with specialist interest in the subject. There are however other remarkable pieces which derive from contact on the Northwest Coast over the 19th and 20th centuries which have not hitherto been published.

In recent years contacts with this Museum have been strengthened due to the writer's past years of residence in and subsequent visits to British Columbia. Consultation with people from the First Nations in British Columbia, and with those responsible for collections in Vancouver and on Vancouver Island, has led to a greater understanding of the cultural importance of the collections at Exeter. Research at the British Columbia Archives and Records Service in Victoria in 1996 led to the dating of a set of objects from a previously unidentified mid-nineteenth century voyage. In 1998 Exeter's historical connections with the Northwest Coast were celebrated when Tim Paul, Hesquiaht Nuu-chah-nulth master carver, along with senior and apprentice carvers, came to Exeter with their families to carve and raise the totem pole, *Ilchinik*, the Whaler. Continuing research on these collections will improve knowledge of their significance still further.

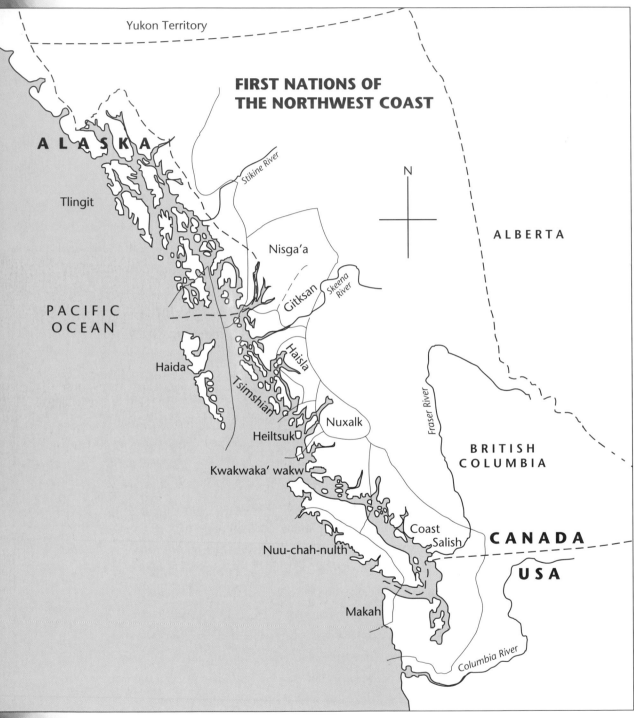

FIRST NATIONS OF
THE NORTHWEST COAST

Yukon Territory

ALASKA

Stikine River

Tlingit

Nisga'a

N

ALBERTA

PACIFIC
OCEAN

Gitksan

Skeena River

Haida

Haisla

Tsimshian

Fraser River

Nuxalk

Heiltsuk

BRITISH
COLUMBIA

Kwakwaka' wakw

Coast
Salish

CANADA

Nuu-chah-nulth

USA

Makah

Columbia River

4. First Nations of the Northwest Coast.

INTRODUCTION

Location and Climate

The Northwest Coast culture area of North America extends from northern Washington State, USA, north through the west coast of British Columbia, Canada, to Alaska's Yakutat Bay. The region is shielded by the Coast Range mountains from the subarctic weather conditions farther inland and warmed by the air of the Japan Current, the Kuroshio. For millennia this narrow strip of mainland, and its many islands, has enabled its peoples to prosper from a wealth of natural resources provided by the land, ocean, rivers and lakes.

The Kuroshio flows north, following the continental shelf some distance offshore. Cold water pushed into the coast by this current creates fog banks that can shroud both sea and shore. When the fog banks turn to cloud and rise over the mountains they fall as rain on the islands and mainland. At times stormy weather beats upon the coast from the North Pacific waters. Rainfall is frequent. Mountains, some glacial, rise from most of the shore's length, extending inland for some 160 km, and steep-sided inlets cut channels into much of the shoreline. There are also many beaches, some of them open to the Pacific Ocean, others nestled in sheltered bays and coves.

Forests blanket thousands of acres of land, from close to the snow line on the mountainsides down to the waters' edge. These forests of tall, mostly coniferous, trees together with prolific moss growth, rotting fallen trees, underbrush, streams and swamps, all contribute to a rich and varied ecosystem. Animal life abounds; bears, cougars, wolves, deer, raccoons, are only a few of the mammals that share this warm, wet region with other wildlife – bald eagles, ravens, waterfowl, migratory hummingbirds and many more species. Its rivers, the spawning grounds for salmon, also yield sturgeon, trout and eulachon (a small, oil-rich fish prized for its use as a condiment and in medicine). Its rocky outcrops and shores are the realm of walrus, seal, sealion and sea otter. Its ocean waters are visited by whales in their annual migrations and stocked with various species of cod, halibut, flounder, herring, smelt and octopus.

The People - and the World that Was

The inhabitants of the Pacific Northwest Coast are not a unified people representing a single nation. Although cultural, environmental and economic backgrounds are common to the Tlingit, Tsimshian, Haida, Nuxalk, Kwakwaka'wakw, Coast Salish and Nuu-chah-nulth and other First Nations, there are many differences in cultural practice. In British Columbia there are thirty First Nations languages, and many different dialects. These nations also developed tribal, or clan divisions according to the expansion of the seven major language groups.

Arriving in the region about 15,000 years ago, the coastal people gradually developed an economy based on fishing, hunting and gathering and advanced food preservation methods. For those who knew where and how to hunt and fish, gather and process, food was plentiful. Seaweed, berries, roots, bulbs and tender plant shoots provided a balance to a diet rich in fish and the meat of sea and land mammals.

Small village settlements of as few as three to as many as twenty big cedar-planked houses each accommodating 30 - 40 people, of usually four closely related families, each family group occupying a sectioned area of the house. These houses were built on the shores of rivers and in the more sheltered bays and coves all along the coast, facing out onto the water. Most of them could be partially deconstructed; the wedge-split wall and roof planks were removable from the framework of massive support posts for loading onto canoes for the move to seasonal camps. On arrival at the campsite the planks were easily fitted onto the uprights and roof posts there. Canoes were dugouts, each made from a single cedar tree and used for travel to other villages to trade, feast, and potlatch. The great canoes made by the Haida were hewn out of massive cedar trees and could reach close to 18.3 metres (60ft) in length. Trading voyages, often of fleets of canoes, might cover 1600 kilometres round trip and last for several months. In spring and summer the canoe became the means by which food was harvested from the ocean, and from beaches distant from the village. As a maritime people, centuries of technological expertise went into the making of fish-hooks, harpoons and spears. Net fishing was also used and weirs and traps were constructed. Oysters, clams, seaweed, fern shoots and berries were collected in burden baskets (number 24) of tightly woven cedar roots.

Social structure was based on class divisions from the highest-ranking chief of each community through the lesser chiefs and their families to commoners and slaves. Inheritance determined rank, although status could be enhanced by marriage, shrewd trading practice and exploitation of resources, as well as by impressive potlatch displays and raids.

Ancestry was traced to animals and to supernatural beings who peopled the world when they took off their masks and transformed into humans. For example, in Haida legend it was Raven, who put the elements of this world in their order, who discovered human beings in a clamshell washed up on the beach.

Kinship, the ties between relatives, determined rights to ceremonial privileges and crests. These ties also determined the right to marry into certain other groups, and to live in a certain household group. Gender and order of birth in a family largely determined the inheritance of an individual. To be the first-born generally ensured the status of heir, the inheritor of family wealth. A first-born woman inherited wealth in trust for her sons. Painted and carved crests commissioned by the chiefs, the motifs owned by them, served as powerful visual statements of prestigious ancestry.

Chiefs owned rights to the control of the best hunting, fishing and plant-collecting areas in their locality, for the benefit of their community. As important was the ownership of honoured names, songs, dances and regalia. Some of these rights came down through inheritance, from the ancestors, while others were acquired according to recognition of deeds through life. Affiliation with other high-status families through marriage accrued prestige in the form of names to be recited, songs and dances to be performed and regalia to be shown at potlatches, contributing to the chief's show of wealth in the wider community.

Probably the most recognised form of crest display on the Northwest Coast today is the totem pole. Before white contact there were four main kinds: the interior house post; the massive house frontal pole; the free-standing memorial pole; the mortuary pole in which a high-ranking chief's remains were placed. Painted screens, ceremonial masks, and decorated clothing and other regalia also displayed ancestral status.

The potlatch has for centuries been the arena where elaborate ceremonial has employed a complexity of symbolism in song and masked and costumed dance. Lineage histories were recited at potlatches in order to confirm chiefly rights and privileges. Social changes brought about by births, marriages and deaths were also publicly proclaimed and recorded. This ceremony was fundamental in holding society together. Although the word 'potlatch', from the Nuu-chah-nulth *patshatl*, meaning 'giving', refers to the latter part of the ceremony where gifts are distributed to invited guests as witnesses to the prestige of the host, it has now come to denote the entire ceremony.

The Royal Albert Memorial Museum holds several items associated with potlatch feasting. The rich and (as I can attest) delicious oil derived from the eulachon, or candle-fish, was favoured among the Kwakwaka'wakw and Nuu-chah-nulth nations as a condiment for dipping salmon and other foods. In other areas, seal grease was preferred. Finely carved dishes and bowls were made as containers for seal grease and eulachon oil. These items were treasured by the families who owned them, brought out for potlatch feasts and put carefully away afterwards. The two Haida frog dishes (catalogue numbers 8 and 9) and the Nuu-chah-nulth Wolf dish (number 5) are fine examples of this tradition, and show evidence of use over a long period. The elaborately carved horn spoons (numbers 1, 2 and 4) and the painted wooden spoons (number 3) were also made specifically for potlatch feasting. A further ceremonial item is the Raven rattle (number 11), once the property of a northern noble. It would have been danced with the hawk face uppermost.

Early European influences

When European explorers ventured into the often stormy waters of the Northwest Coast and entered First Nations territories they discovered that the coastal inhabitants were a confident and assertive people, extremely shrewd and adept in all matters of trade. Eager to barter and fully aware of the value of their trade items, the coastal people already had a long history of inter-tribal trade.

Along the central coast virtually all contact outside the Northwest Coast culture area was prevented by impenetrable forests and impassable mountain ranges. In the north, the Tlingit and Tsimshian had trade contacts with the interior Athabaskans, accounting for their use of skin clothing with porcupine quill and European glass bead decoration in place of woven cedar bark clothing. There was considerable exchange among the Tlingit, Athabaskan, Eyak and the Pacific Inuit.

The Tsinúk people, living on the north side of the Columbia River, were successful middlemen, between the southern Northwest Coast peoples and other groups, at the inter-tribal trading area known as the Dalles, also on the Columbia River. Foodstuffs, including dried salmon and fish oil, cedar bark, mountain goat wool and animal pelts, were commodities exchanged there for items such as abalone shell from California. Before the arrival of European voyagers, early Russian fur traders introduced goods from China, with ancient Chinese coins being favoured by northern groups for use as clothing decoration and personal ornament.

In his journal for 30 March 1778 while anchored at Nootka Sound* in Nuu-chah-nulth territory, Captain Cook recorded that the traders brought pelts, in particular those of the sea otter, to exchange for European knives and chisels, pieces of iron and tin, nails and buttons.

White traders made their fortunes taking highly valued sea otter furs to sell in China. This was a highly lucrative trade for the first forty years after initial white contact, when more than a quarter of a million sea otter pelts were sent to Canton from the Northwest Coast. In the first two decades of the nineteenth century over-hunting led to a reduction in the viability of the sea otter pelt trade, but other fur-bearing animals were available. Between 1800 and 1850 the Hudson's Bay Company set up a series of trading posts in the region to further exploit this resource.

Northwest Coast First Nations society, based on wealth display, suffered a tremendous upheaval as a result of this European commercial interest. The manufacture of prestige goods for potlatch distribution was slow and laborious. Exchanging the more easily acquired furs for store goods led to a radical increase in the frequency of potlatching, changing its basic nature to one of rivalry and competition in wealth display. The safeguarding of trade possibilities led many away from traditional subsistence activities. Tensions mounted on both sides, usually as a result of misunderstanding of local customs and rights. For example, Europeans killed a chief over a petty disagreement; retaliatory attacks were made on European trading vessels, in turn leading to villages, canoes and other property being smashed and burned and their communities dispersed. Hostilities between the First Nations themselves intensified in the 1830s and 40s and conflict became increasingly deadly with the availability of firearms.

*It was Cook who named Nootka Sound. When his ships were approaching the village of Yuquot, in Nuu-chah-nulth territory, the Chief sent out four of his men to investigate. They told Cook, "You go around the harbour" (to find better anchorage), *Nu-tka-icim*. Having no comprehension of the language, Cook assumed he was being told the place-name.

Repression and Subjugation

By 1858 the government had gained full control over Vancouver Island and the mainland, when both were declared British colonies. Increasingly, First Nations sovereignty was denied, land was taken and the indigenous peoples were granted small areas of reservation land. Forced into a cash-economy, denied control of commercial resources, traditional lands and fishing and hunting grounds, the dawn of a new era for increasing numbers of white settlers held little promise for First Nations peoples.

Europeans and Euro-Americans carried diseases to the Northwest Coast that were previously unknown, with truly devastating results. Smallpox, tuberculosis, influenza, measles and other viral infections killed the inhabitants of entire villages in some regions from the 1850s until the 1880s. A death rate of 90 – 95% among First Nations communities was the direct result of successive waves of these epidemics. Moreover, sectarian missionaries and government agents in turn preached salvation and assimilation, so that the few survivors of the epidemics struggled to retain a hold on their traditional ways. At the end of the 19th century it was the assumption of many white Canadians that the "heathen savages", as First Nations peoples were then generally considered by the dominant, white Christian culture, were headed for inevitable extinction.

The government established British Columbia as a Canadian province in 1871, with no government recognition of First Nations territories as sovereign nations. In 1876, the passing of the Indian Act made all Native people in Canada the administrative wards of the federal government. No provision was made for the participation of indigenous populations in the structuring of the law.

A few treaties relating to Coast Salish lands on Vancouver Island were negotiated by the Hudson's Bay Company (HBC) before the island became a British Colony. Formal permission was also given by the chiefs of four Southern Kwakwaka'wakw groups allowing the HBC to use land for Fort Rupert. The HBC 'paid' for the land with trade goods. Local agreements were also signed by chiefs to permit trading stores, mission schools and churches to be built on their lands. Neither British Columbian, nor later Canadian law resulted in any official land settlement. Despite this fact, federal agents took over all control of land and resources.

From the beginning, missionaries and federal officials had opposed traditional First Nations ceremonial practices, citing them as responsible for wastefulness and indigence. In 1885 the government passed a law to ban the potlatch and other important ceremonies, with imprisonment and seizure of potlatch goods and regalia as punishment for its contravention. Following the Kwakwaka'wakw potlatch of December 1921 hosted by the Cranmer family, 23 people who attended the gathering received prison sentences of two months duration, and four were sentenced to six months. Treasured family regalia was seized and shipped to Ottawa. Thirty-five pieces were sold on to the Museum of the American Indian in New York for $291. The bulk of the collection, valued at a mere $1456, was retained by the National Museum of Canada (now the Canadian Museum of Civilization) and the rest was kept by the Royal Ontario Museum.

First Nations people in British Columbia were by this time divided on the future of their traditions and culture. Individuals and groups who saw Christianity and assimilation as the new way forward, and perhaps the only way, and so opposed the perpetuation of their old customs, endorsed the anti-potlatch law. Others kept up the potlatch in secret, travelling to remote villages beyond easy surveillance by government agents.

Residential missionary schooling was thoroughly established by the Canadian government at the beginning of the 20th century. Children were removed from their families and boarded at the schools. They were forbidden to speak their own languages; a common punishment was to wash out the mouths of the offenders with soap and water. Young adults emerged from these authoritarian institutions unable to fit back fully into their own communities yet still rejected by white society. Memories of this harsh and repressive system of 'education' remain vivid in the minds of many of the elderly and those of middle age even today.

These times were not without resistance to subjugation and to attempts to assimilate First Nations peoples into Canadian society and culture. As early as the 1880s First Nations workers were striking for improvement in conditions and for higher wages.

Resurgence

After 1930, First Nations' populations began to increase in British Columbia, an increase partly responsible for a resurgence of confidence and assertiveness. In 1931 the Native Brotherhood of British Columbia was formed by First Nations' representatives to protect the rights of all coastal peoples. In 1936 the Kwakwaka'wakw, then known as the Kwakiutl, founded the Pacific Coast Native Fishermen's Association, a labour union for cannery workers and fishermen. Both groups joined forces in 1942. In 1970 the Union of British Columbia Indian Chiefs was founded, which then joined with Native organisations from other Canadian provinces to create the National Indian Brotherhood (NIB). The primary concern of the NIB was in gaining equality and opportunity in the post-war white world. Demands were for more schools and hospitals, for non-denominational education, for voting rights in federal elections, negotiation of land rights and the reduction of controls imposed by government Indian agents.

Proposals for an extensive revision of the Indian Act in 1951 were met with criticism by First Nations peoples, Civil Liberties and other groups across Canada. As a result prohibitions against cultural practices were dropped from the statute books, permitting the potlatch and other ceremonies to be practised openly. Potlatch paraphernalia seized during the years of banning has in part been returned: the Canadian Museum of Civilization returned its portion in 1979 and 1980, followed soon after by the Royal Ontario Museum's share of the goods.

The legality of imposed land division continues to be debated in federal court. First Nations are demanding recognition of rights to fishing areas and other resources, as well as to self-government. Wider alliances have been made with organisations representing indigenous minorities world-wide. Big business interests, particularly those of the logging companies, compound the complexity of these issues, but progress is being made.

Very few traditional villages and seasonal campsites remain today. In some areas the epidemics wiped out entire communities, in others the survivors were too broken to resist government removals to reservation lands. Most of the great houses of massive cedar posts and planks were abandoned, their remnants slowly reclaimed by the forests to this day. But territories and tradition are far from forgotten. The sea and forests still sustain First Nations peoples physically as well as culturally. Although modern fishing methods are most often used, traditional ways of gathering and preparing food are also practised.

The economy of British Columbia is based largely on fisheries and forestry as it was in the past. The people and the world that was are now absorbed into the global society. First Nations peoples and communities are committed to working to secure mutually beneficial and productive working relationships with industry and government to ensure sustainable resources and equal employment opportunities into the future.

In the education system, children are being taught their own languages in native run schools, and learning about the nation's history from a First Nations' perspective.

The suppression of Northwest Coast culture disrupted the continuity of its art forms, for some nations more than others. The artists of today continue to research their heritage using items in family and museum collections as reference, as well as consulting with the elders of their communities. Ancient themes continue to be depicted in wood on such items as totem poles, masks, bentwood boxes, rattles, dishes and bowls. The skill of fine basket making in cedar bark, roots and sedges has been handed down through the generations, and makers of canoes, and canoe models are as proficient today as their predecessors were in past centuries. Haida argillite carving that began as a commercial venture in the early 19th century has retained its popularity among tourists and collectors. The media of gold and silver jewellery, and limited edition silkscreen prints, have added new dimensions to the art forms of past tradition. Northwest Coast artists continue to serve their originating communities and to contribute to a unique and vibrant culture.

Archaeological excavations have revealed that the Northwest Coast art tradition dates back nearly 3000 years. In the past wealth displays and gift giving at potlatches served to encourage the arts. With the resurgence of traditional values, First Nations' artists are once again serving their communities, in the making of masks and other regalia for ceremonial, in the carving of totem poles to celebrate important community events, and through income earned from commissioned work outside of their local communities. Many of today's artists have international status and their works are sought after by individual collectors, art galleries and museums world-wide. One such artist is Tim Paul, of the Hesquiaht Nuu-chah-nulth, who was commissioned to carve a totem pole for Exeter Museum. The pole (number 79), *Ilchinik* (the Whaler), was carved at this museum and raised with due ceremony in the Americas section of the World Cultures Gallery in June 1998. *Ilchinik* stands beside those items collected on the voyages of Captains James Cook and George Vancouver in the 18th century, and other items, of no less importance, brought back to England by European travellers and generously given to this museum. Some of those stories have been revealed, some remain to be discovered.

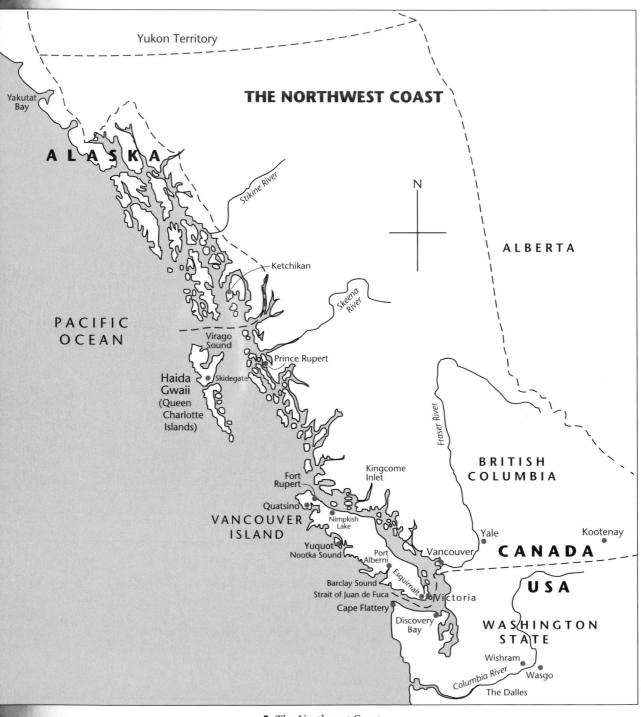

THE NORTHWEST COAST

Yukon Territory

Yakutat
Bay

ALASKA

Stikine River

N

ALBERTA

Ketchikan

PACIFIC
OCEAN

Skeena
River

Virago
Sound

Prince Rupert

Haida
Gwaii
(Queen
Charlotte
Islands)

Skidegate

Fraser River

BRITISH
COLUMBIA

Kingcome
Inlet

Fort
Rupert

Quatsino

VANCOUVER
ISLAND

Nimpkish
Lake

Yale

Kootenay

Vancouver

CANADA

Yuquot
Nootka Sound

Port
Alberni

Esquimalt

USA

Barclay Sound
Strait of Juan de Fuca

Victoria

Cape Flattery

WASHINGTON
STATE

Discovery
Bay

Wishram

Columbia River

Wasgo

The Dalles

5. The Northwest Coast.

COLLECTORS AND DONORS OF
NORTHWEST COAST ITEMS IN THE MUSEUM

J. D. Agassiz

James David Agassiz began his naval career in 1815 and was promoted to Lieutenant in 1829. From 1844 – 6 he sailed as First Lieutenant on the voyage of HMS *America* in the Pacific, with Captain John Gordon. Items donated to the museum by Agassiz were collected by him on this voyage, from Port Discovery (now called Discovery Bay) in 1845. The purpose of this visit to the Northwest Coast was to represent British interests in the region during the Oregon crisis of 1845, and to oppose American encroachment in the Columbia River area.

T. N. Brushfield

One item, the model head canoe with four paddles, number 73 in the catalogue list, was collected by William Eales in about 1837. It was donated in 1911 by Mrs. Hannah Brushfield in memory of her late husband Thomas Nadauld Brushfield (1827-1910). His relationship to William Eales has not yet been researched and at present it is not known under what circumstances the canoe model changed hands.

Described in the Dictionary of National Biography, 2nd Supplement, as a 'Lunacy specialist and antiquarian', Brushfield, devoted the years after his retirement to the study of the life of Sir Walter Raleigh. He settled in Budleigh Salterton and was a popular lecturer as well as founder of the Devon and Cornwall Record Society. Brushfield's collection of items associated with Raleigh are held by Exeter Public Library, as are his collection of lantern slides.

William Buckingham 1835 – ?

Born in Burrington, Devon, William Buckingham was a solicitor, alderman, and magistrate in Exeter, and clerk to the Exeter Turnpike Trust. He served as Mayor of Exeter in 1857. In 1875 he donated a collection of ethnographic material to the Royal Albert Memorial Museum from the Pacific, South America and Vancouver Island. No information has yet been found of when or how he acquired these items.

Devon & Exeter Institution

The core of the Museum's early ethnographic collections was formed by the Devon and Exeter Institution, a local philosophical and literary society established in 1813 in Cathedral Close, Exeter, and still functioning today. Its collections included major groups of Polynesian and Polar material and a miscellany of material from other parts of the world. Sadly the documentation preserved by the Institution is very slight. Most of the collection seems to have been assembled between 1813 and 1834. The entire ethnographic holdings of the Institution were transferred to Queen Street upon the foundation of this museum after 1868 but by that stage the museum function of the Institution had long been defunct. Pearce (*Arts of Polynesia*, Exeter Museums, 1973) has suggested that much of the collection derived from Cook's voyages, but John Allan has re-examined the evidence (*Artefacts at Exeter City Museums from Bligh's Second Voyage to Tahiti*, published in Pacific Arts, July 1995) and shown that the most substantial element in it came from Bligh's second voyage to Tahiti in 1791-3. The Northwest Coast material clearly doesn't come from that source but presumably comes from at least one other early voyage to the Northwest Coast, Hawaii and New Zealand in the late 18th century or the beginning of the 19th century.

Edgar Dewdney 1835 – 1916

Items from British Columbia's Northwest Coast donated in 1927 by Edgar Dewdney's second wife, Blanche Elizabeth Plantagenet.

Edgar Dewdney was born on November 5th 1835, in Devon. He was educated in the county as a civil engineer. He left England for British Columbia, Canada, in May 1859 at the age of 23. Between 1859 and 1872 he travelled widely in the province as a surveyor to town planners and road builders. At this early stage in the colonial history of British Columbia towns were being laid out, and plots were being sold at auction to white settlers. Dewdney was also involved in preliminary surveys for the Canadian Pacific Railroad. In 1868 he began a career in government. Over the next two decades he represented the Kootenay and Yale districts in the Legislative Council, served as Indian Commissioner, and later Lieutenant Governor, for the Northwest Territories, represented East Assiniboia in the House of Commons and held the portfolios of Minister of the Interior and Superintendent-General of Indian affairs in the cabinets of Sir John A. Macdonald and his successor, Sir John Abbott. In 1893 he was appointed Lieutenant-Governor of British Columbia. In November 1897, at the conclusion of this term of office, he retired from political life and settled in Victoria where he pursued his private interests as a mining-broker and insurance and financial agent. The reason that Dewdney bequeathed his collection to Exeter Museum is stated in a letter from his widow to the Museum dated March 12th 1920:

Dear Sir –

Some years ago my husband and I were on a visit to Exeter while home from British Columbia. We saw in the Museum an Indian Chief's shirt, I think it had belonged to 'Crowfoot' Chief of the Blackfeet Indians. My husband was very interested having known the Chief well, also having a unique collection of Indian Curios of his own. He told me that after his death he would like me to offer some of this collection to the Exeter Museum.

The 'Indian Chief's shirt' and other items of Blackfoot costume were collected by Cecil Denny of the Canadian North West Mounted Police who had been a colleague of Edgar Dewdney.

The 1920 donation by Mrs Dewdney of items from the Plains, Subarctic and Eastern Woodlands regions was followed in 1927 by a further gift that included the 16 items from the Northwest Coast listed in this catalogue.

6. The Honourable Edgar Dewdney photographed in April 1883 in his official uniform of Lieutenant-Governor of the Northwest Territories.
(Photographer unknown.)

Revd. F.J. Dyson 1864 – 1935

In 1931 Reverend Francis Julian Dyson donated about 160 items from various parts of the world: Syria, Palestine, Asia, Australasia, South Africa and the Americas. It would appear that this material was collected between the years 1885 and 1889 when Dyson sailed around the world.

He graduated from Trinity College in 1899 with a Masters degree, presumably in theology. He then pursued a career in the church, begun in 1890, that was to occupy the rest of his life. His appointments in Devon began in Littleham, Exmouth, where he was a Curate from 1911-17 and Vicar from 1917-23. From 1926-29 he was Rural Dean of Aylsebeare and Vicar to the same parish from 1923-31.

7. Haida feasting dish carved in the form of a frog, rear view. Collected by FJ Dyson between 1885-9.

Bradley Gregory ? – 1884

Son of Captain Thomas Gregory RN of Exeter, Bradley Gregory entered the Royal Navy as Assistant Surgeon in 1859 on HMS *Amphion* in the Mediterranean. He was promoted to Staff Surgeon in August 1870 and to Fleet Surgeon in 1881, in the year before his retirement. The Northwest Coast material donated to Exeter Museum by Bradley Gregory in 1868 was collected during his period of office as Assistant Surgeon aboard HMS *Devastation* in the Pacific from 1863 to about 1866.

From 1867 to 1880 Gregory served aboard several of Her Majesty's Ships: *Rodney*, China Station, appointed January 1867; *Spiteful*, Cape of Good Hope and West Coast of Africa, appointed July 1873; *Pembroke*, flag ship of the Admiral Superintendent, *Chatham*, for service at Melville Hospital, appointed September 1877; *Phoenix*, North America and West Indies Station, appointed April 1880.

F.W.L. Ross 1793 – 1860

In the early years of his life Francis William Locke Ross served as an officer in the British navy. For many years he lived at Broadway House, Topsham. It was apparently there that he opened a museum to the public, containing specimens that reflected his lifelong interest in natural history and related sciences. In 1865 the contents of Ross's museum were transferred to Exeter Museum. This international collection of 5000 items, principally natural history specimens, included 115 ethnographic items. The set of Haida gambling sticks E780 formed a part of this bequest. Documentation at the time of accession into this museum reveals that they were collected by the captain of the *Trincomalee*, on her 1852 – 56 voyage, Admiral Wallace Houstoun.

Admiral W. Houstoun 1811 – 1891

In 1852 Admiral Wallace Houstoun captained HMS *Trincomalee*, a frigate built at the yards of the East India Company in Bombay in 1817, when it was sent to the west coast of North America to join the Pacific Squadron to protect British interests in the region. Houstoun Passage and Trincomalee Channel, both in the approaches to Vancouver, are names that commemorate this voyage to the Pacific Northwest.

The following is an extract from Houstoun's 'Journal and Letter Book' addressed to Rear Admiral Fairfax Moresby, Commander in Chief, dated 2nd January 1854:

We arrived at Virago Sound (Queen Charlottes Islands) on the evening of Wednesday the 7th of September; The next day a great many canoes came alongside, the greatest number that day about 40 containing something like 400 men and women amongst these were several Chiefs, but not Edensaw the Chief of the North Island Tribe, the nearest tribe to our Anchorage, he was absent at Kugany on the opposite Island about 30 Miles off.

I had been given to understand that the Indians held great-guns very cheap, that many believed they were of no use; so I was very glad to find so good a place (and the presence of so many) to practice. We fired this day 28 shells, the practice at 1200 yards was exceedingly good 25 shells bursting as intended immediately above the Target; the Indians were very surprised and pleased, fully entering into the principle of the bursting properties of the shell.

8. Portrait of Admiral Wallace Houstoun.
(Photo courtesy of HMS Trincomalee Trust.)

The Target, which was four casks on a skeleton frame, 6½ feet square with a centre cask and shaft, was struck 25 times (out of 81 shot); The Midshipman and boys had an upper deck gun; the rest of the boys another, the Marines another, the Main deck guns their own crews; They changed rounds every time, so very few had a second shot. The target was knocked all to pieces; the practice could not have been better.

Mr. Stuart - the gentleman on board us belonging to the Hudson Bay Company's service learnt at different times from those of the Indians who could talk the Chinook Language that all were very much surprised, some said, why one or two of those would blow us all up, indeed on the 17th John Edensaw came on board, the best thing nearly he said was that the Indians had told him about the shells, adding, he could not believe it unless he saw it, on which one was fired with an Inch Fuse which burst famously at 400 yards. We also fired from the boat Gun a shell, loaded with Musket balls, and also a rocket. This very intelligent chief was perfectly satisfied and fully understood the nature of these projectiles...I consider this part of Queen Charlottes Islands very central for seeing and being seen by the different Tribes, we saw more than 1200 Indians (and many more were on their way to us) the Advantages of Virago Sound for ingress and egress and its security as an Anchorage cannot well be exceeded.

We left Virago Sound on Tuesday Afternoon the 20th of September on Sunday the 25th we got a sight of Mount Columbus, but the next day set in with fog which continued for four days, beautiful bright weather and calms and Light North Easterly winds succeeded, and prevented our reaching Esquimalt until the 5th of October.

Restoration of the HMS *Trincomalee*, the second oldest ship afloat and one of the world's most important historic ships, began in 1990. She is presently berthed at Jackson Dock, Hartlepool and is the centrepiece of the Maritime Heritage Centre.

W.B. Scott 1807 – 1884

William Bower Scott was born and lived in Chudleigh, Devon, and was the son of Vice-Admiral Scott.

He worked as a solicitor in Chudleigh but his principal interests were ornithology, ichthyology and other branches of natural history. He inherited the collection of Northwest Coast ethnographic material from his uncle, James Woodward Scott, and donated this material to the Royal Albert Memorial Museum in 1869.

J.W. Scott 1780 – 1803

James Woodward Scott was born in Plymouth. He was 12 years old when he began his service as Midshipman aboard the *Chatham*, armed tender to the *Discovery*, and later on the *Discovery*, on Captain George Vancouver's voyage to the Pacific and the Northwest Coast of North America, 1791-5.

In the course of this voyage Vancouver was able to map out a large proportion of the western and north-western coasts of North America for the first time. The primary purpose of the voyage was to investigate the possible existence of a Northwest Passage from Canada's interior through to the Pacific Coast. A further objective was to settle a territorial dispute between Britain and Spain over the ownership of the island we now know as Vancouver Island. Vancouver anchored at Yuquot (Place-that-is-hit-by-winds-from-all-directions), then called Friendly Cove, in Nuu-chah-nulth territory in August 1792 and left to sail south the following October.

Scott died in fighting against the French in the Napoleonic wars.

H. Vaughan

Items donated by Henry Vaughan were purchased by a relative, "Vaughan of Devonshire", in 1806 at the sale of the Leverian Museum collection. In 1781 Sir Ashton Lever acquired many items from the voyages of Captain James Cook that he then exhibited at Leicester House in Leicester Square, London. The entire contents of the Leverian Museum were sold by lottery in 1786 and the winner, James Parkinson, sold on the collection, this time by auction, in 1806.

More than 7800 lots were auctioned over a period of 65 days. There are five surviving sales catalogues. These are annotated with the names of the buyers, and the prices the lots were sold for. Vaughan of Devonshire purchased 52 lots of natural history specimens and 18 lots of Pacific artefacts, including the Northwest Coast items listed in this catalogue.

3

CATALOGUE

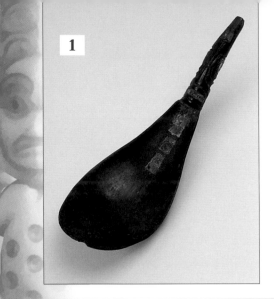

1

3

5

10

8

9

11

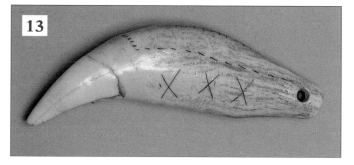

12

13

20

21

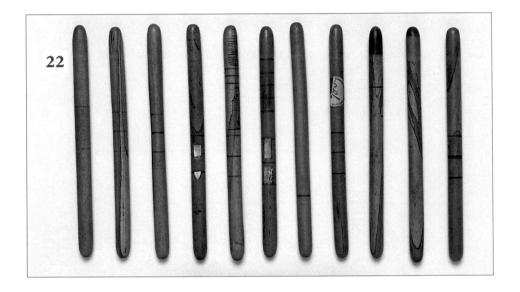

22

24

23

25

27

29

31

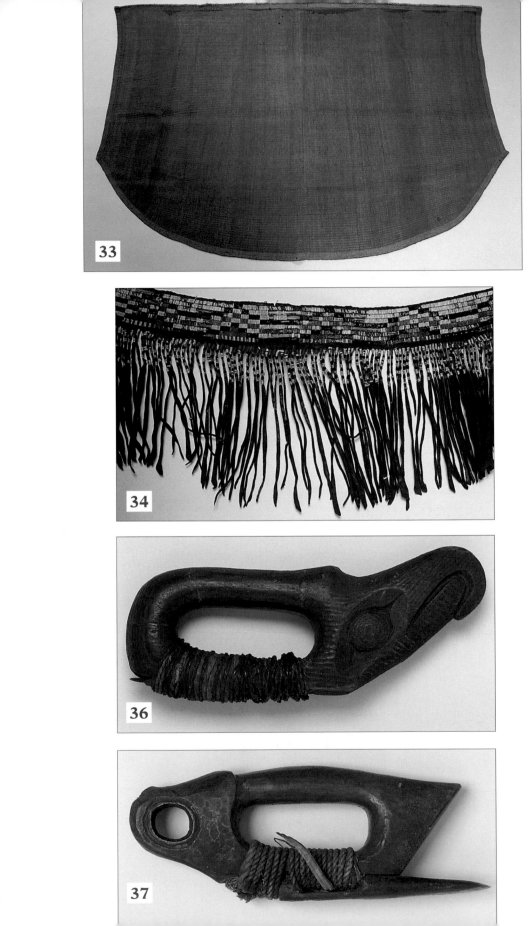

33

34

36

37

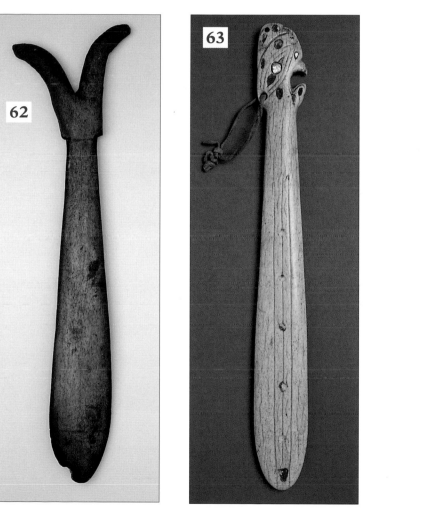

79

72

74

75

77

76

78

80

CHIEf's Box Killer Whale   - ORIGINAL -   Tom Paul June 20

A: POTLATCH & CEREMONIAL

Cat No.	Name	Description of item	Size in mm	Collector/ Donor
1*	**Feasting spoon.** *Mountain goat horn, abalone shell, resin.*	Kwakwaka'wakw nation. This spoon has the head of an unidentified animal carved on the handle. The process of making dishes, bowls and spoons from goat or sheep horn involved steaming and shaping in a mould before carving. The Kwa'kwala word for abalone shell is *eeksam*. Along with number 2, this spoon may originate from Fort Rupert, Quatsino, Nimpkish areas. Collected on Vancouver Island between 1863 and 1866.	L. 174	*Gregory* E770
2*	**Feasting spoon.** *Mountain goat horn.*	Kwakwaka'wakw nation. The figure on the handle of this spoon may be a human in spirit form. Collected on Vancouver Island between 1863 and 1866.	L. 161	*Gregory* E771
3*	**Two Feasting spoons.** *Wood, red and black pigment.*	Haida or Tsimshian nation. Both spoons are painted to represent salmon, one spoon showing the mouth closed and the other with the mouth open. The style of painting would point to a northern source. Presented to the Museum in 1869.	L. 194 L. 230	*Whitney* E786 E787
4*	**Feasting spoon: *Sdláagwaal xasáa.*** *Mountain goat horn, copper.*	Haida nation. A feasting spoon made of two pieces of horn, the handle and bowl carved separately and joined with three copper rivets. It may not be possible to discover what, if anything, the individual figures carved on this spoon represent as a whole since so many stories from the past have been lost. It would have been made for a person of high rank. The illustration, Fig.5, shows the figural design 'unwrapped' from the handle, which makes it easier to see the relationship between two-dimensional and three-dimensional Northwest Coast art forms. The literal meaning of *Sdláagwaal xasáa* is 'two-piece horn spoon'. Made in the 19th century.	L. 245	*Lega-Weekes* 43/1949.1
5*	**Feasting dish.** *Wood, otter teeth, pigment.*	Nuu-chah-nulth nation. An oil or grease dish carved at one end in the form of Wolf, with a human astride the neck. At the other end of the dish is an unidentified creature. This piece would have been designed and made specifically for the host of a potlatch. It has been suggested that the overall style of this dish shows an influence from the Pacific. The early Nuu-chah-nulth eye-forms place the making of this item in the 18th century. Collected on the voyage of HMS *America* in 1845. Published in Gunther, 1962, p.99.	L. 365	*Agassiz* E798

*Illustrated

Cat No.	Name	Description of item	Size in mm	Collector/ Donor
6*	**Bowl.** *Mountain sheep horn.*	Wishxam/Wasgo region, Columbia River Plateau. The carving style of the Salishan speaking peoples of the Columbia River area of Washington State employs a formal surface decoration that differs from the figural imagery of the more northerly regions. These elaborately carved bowls, (numbers 6 and 7) with their high raised ends and designs of interlocking triangles, were used for ceremonial purposes. Transferred to the Museum in 1865, and likely to have been made in the late 18th to mid 19th century. Published in Gunther, 1962, p.99 and Haberland, 1964, p.76.	Dia. 200	*Ross* E1292
7*	**Bowl.** *Mountain sheep horn.*	Wishxam/Wasgo region, Columbia River Plateau. Transferred to the Museum in 1865, and likely to have been made in the late 18th to mid 19th century.	Dia. 180	*Ross* E1293
8*	**Feasting dish.** *Wood, oil/grease.*	Haida nation. Eulachon oil dish carved in the form of a frog. From the oil-blackened wood and amount of wear on this dish and 80/1931.146 (number 9), it would appear that they were both in use a long time before being collected. Items such as these were generally curated within the family of ownership, being used on important occasions and then returned to storage. Collected between 1885 and 1889 and likely to have been made in the 18th century.	L. 119	*Dyson* 80/1931.145
9*	**Feasting dish.** *Wood, (suffused with oil/grease).*	Haida nation. Eulachon oil dish carved at both ends with the face and front legs of frog. Stained black from oil or grease. Collected between 1885 and 1889 and likely to have been made in the 18th century.	L. 118	*Dyson* 80/1931.146
10*	**Portrait figure.** *Wood, pigment.*	Northern Northwest Coast, perhaps Heiltsuk nation. A three-quarter length or seated male figure wearing a garment with a high collar, edged in red. The hairstyle and features are European. Portrait figures such as this were often carved specifically for highly skilled drama presentations that took place during potlatches. Made in the early 19th century.	H. 305	*Allford* 31/1951.1
11*	**Raven rattle.** *Wood, pigment, pebbles, dried peas*	Northern Northwest Coast, perhaps Heiltsuk nation or Nuxalk nation. A noble's dance rattle. Raven forms the main body of the rattle. On his back lies a shaman, connected via the tongue to the beak of a kingfisher. Two frogs sit astride the shaman's chest. Raven also has a frog in his beak. The underside is carved in shallow relief, and painted, characteristically in the form of the face of a hawk. When Raven rattles are danced they are usually held upside-down, as shaking the rattle upright could cause the raven to fly away. Made in the early 19th century.	L. 393	*Allford* 31/1951.2

*Illustrated

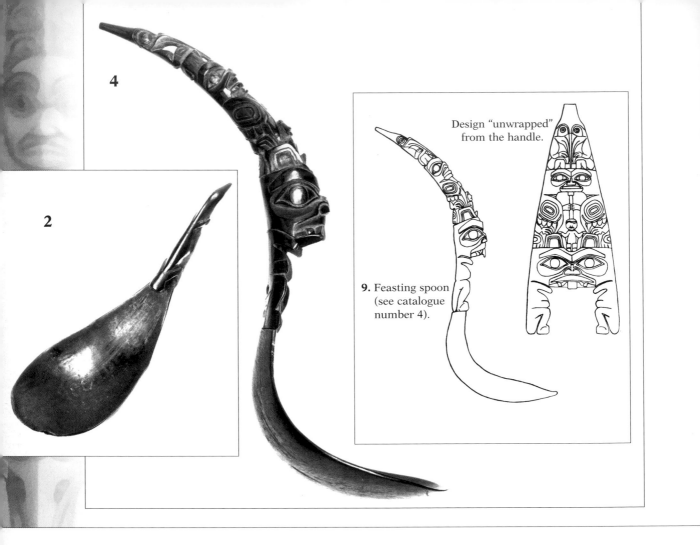

4

2

Design "unwrapped" from the handle.

9. Feasting spoon (see catalogue number 4).

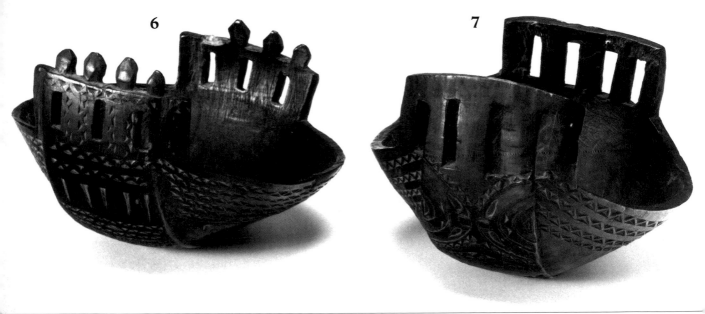

6

7

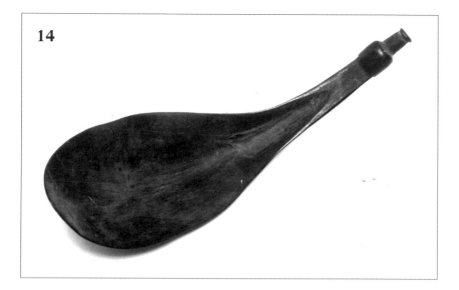

14

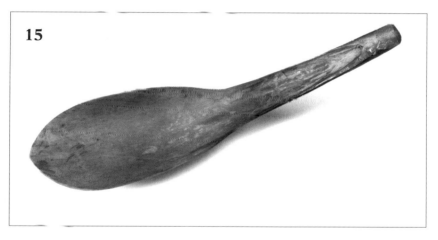

15

16

B: Shamanic Items

Cat No.	Name	Description of item	Size in mm	Collector/ Donor
12*	**Pendant amulet.** *Bear's tooth.*	Tlingit nation. An amulet carved in the form of Wolf, the head beneath the body, the tail curled. A perforation is drilled into base of the tooth for suspension. Collected by Midshipman James Woodward Scott between 1792 and 1794 on the 1791–95 Pacific voyage of Captain George Vancouver. For illustration see Gunther, 1962, p.76, Pearce, 1976, p.60 and Wardwell, 1996, no.269.	L. 94	*Scott (ex Vancouver)* E792a
13*	**Pendant amulet.** *Bear's tooth.*	Tlingit nation. One side is incised with three X marks and a line of short strokes. The other side is incised with a ladder-like pattern. The upper, convex surface carries an incised line crossed with short strokes at right angles. A perforation is drilled into the base of the tooth for suspension. Collected by Midshipman James Woodward Scott between 1792 and 1794 on the 1791–95 Pacific voyage of Captain George Vancouver.	L. 98	*Scott (ex Vancouver)* E792b

C: Domestic Items

Cat No.	Name	Description of item	Size in mm	Collector/ Donor
14*	**Spoon.** *Mountain goat horn.*	Northwest Coast. Steam-bent spoon with a decorated handle finial. Transferred to the Museum in 1872. Collected in the late 18th to early 19th century.	L. 158	*Devon and Exeter Institution* E1754
15*	**Spoon.** *Mountain goat or sheep horn.*	Northwest Coast. A plain and unadorned spoon of pale coloured horn. This spoon and number 16 are styles that are common all over the coast, either made in several areas or widely traded. Collected between 1885 and 1889.	L. 277	*Dyson* 80/1931.148
16*	**Spoon.** *Wood.*	Northwest Coast. A plain spoon of wood. Collected between 1885 and 1889.	L. 251	*Dyson* 80/1931.149
17*	**Spoon.** *Mountain goat horn.*	Northwest Coast. A small, plain horn spoon, the handle tapering to a point. A label on the underside of the bowl reads: *'From the Indian Bazaar, 36, Johnson Street, Victoria, British Columbia.'* Collected between 1885 and 1889.	L. 146	*Dyson* 80.1931.150
18*	**Spoon.** *Mountain goat horn.*	Northwest Coast. A small, plain horn spoon, similar to number 17 and probably purchased by the Reverend Dyson at the 'Indian Bazaar' on Johnson Street in Victoria. Collected between 1885 and 1889.	L. 145	*Dyson* 80.1931.151
19*	**Dish.** *Mountain sheep horn.*	Salish nation. A dish or bowl, the underside of the handle decorated with incised lines. Collected in 1845 on the voyage of HMS *America*.	L. 206	*Agassiz* E795

*Illustrated

Cat No.	Name	Description of item	Size in mm	Collector/ Donor
20*	**Dish.** *Cedar.*	Kwakwaka'wakw or Haida nation. A grease dish or food dish carved in the form of a flounder. The word in Kwa'kwala for flounder is *pa-ees*. Made in the 19th century.	L. 273	*Weston-super-Mare Museum* 64/1974.43
21*	**Dish.** *Cedar.*	Kwakwaka'wakw or Haida nation. A grease dish or food dish carved in the form of a sealion or beaver. A label formerly attached to the inside of this dish reads: *Calabash or dish. Yellow cedar wood. Carved by the last unbaptized heathen man in Kilhatlah (BC) named Allan Laka [pronounced Allaan-Lakhuh] or as he was named by the children 'Nbibs Jonathan' or the uncle of Jonathan. Presented by Rev. R W and Mrs Gurd CMS. 10 Sept 1902. North Pacific Mission.* 'CMS' is the Church Missionary Society, now known as the Church Mission Society, whose work to spread the Christian gospel in Canada began in 1822. 'Kilhatlah' may be a mis-spelling of Kitkatla, in coastal Tsimshian territory south of Prince Rupert on the British Columbia mainland. If the location was Kilhatlah, as documented on the label, it no longer exists as a place name. Many similar-sounding names on the coast were lost during the years of epidemics when so many people died, causing villages to be abandoned. Made in the 19th century.	L. 270	*Gurd, via Weston-super-Mare Museum* 64/1974.56
22*	**Gambling sticks.** *Maple, abalone, pigment.*	Haida nation. Gambling games were common among the Haida as among other Northwest Coast nations. One of the most popular games was played with sets of cylindrical sticks of bone or of polished wood, generally yew, some of which were elaborately carved or painted. The number of sticks in each set could reach seventy. Of the twelve sticks shown here, ten have red and black painted bands, and two have painted bands and inlays of abalone shell. These twelve could be two sets of six sticks, as one stick in each set is always differentiated from the others by being either more or less elaborately decorated. This is the *djîl*, or bait stick, also called the kick or king stick. The game was played by shuffling and concealing the sticks in shredded cedar bark, making from two to four piles in view of the opponent. The opponent scored or lost points by guessing in which pile the *djîl* was hidden. Collected by Admiral Wallace Houstoun in 1853 on the voyage of HMS *Trincomalee*.	L. 125 (each)	*Ross (ex Houstoun)* E 780
23*	**Basket.** *Cedar root, cherry bark.*	Salish nation. A flat-based, rectangular basket. Bundle coil construction of cedar root skin strips with red cherry bark tucked overlay (imbrication). The geometric design, in this instance representing butterflies, is one of several traditional motifs. This basket was collected in the Fraser River region, and at the time of receipt into the Museum (1927) was documented as being over 100 years old. Collected by Edgar Dewdney in the late 19th or early 20th century. Published in Pearce, 1974, p.46.	L. 405	*Dewdney* 70/1927.6

*Illustrated

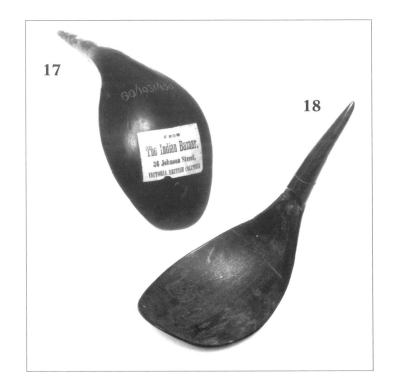

17

18

19

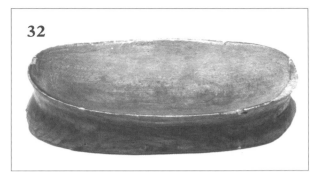

32

26

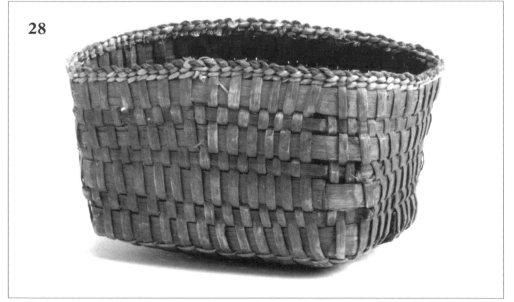

28

Cat No.	Name	Description of item	Size in mm	Collector/ Donor
24*	**Basket.** *Cedar root, cherry bark.*	Salish nation. A flat based, rectangular burden basket. Root strip bundle coil over-sewn with root skin, with tucked overlay (imbrication) design in red cherry bark. This basket shows a great deal of wear. The holes at the rim are evidence that straps were attached, for carrying the basket slung over the back. Collected by Edgar Dewdney in the late 19th or early 20th century and of a similar age to number 23. Published in Pearce, 1974, p.46.	L. 480	*Dewdney* 70/1927.7
25*	**Basket.** *Sedges.*	Nuu-chah-nulth nation. A flat based oval basket with sloping sides made using a wrapping technique over a foundation of verticals and horizontals. Rim folded in. Collected by Edgar Dewdney in the late 19th or early 20th century.	L. 230	*Dewdney* 70/1927.8
26*	**Basket.** *Cedar bark, sedge.*	Nuu-chah-nulth nation. A flat based rectangular basket with outward curving sides. The centre of the base is cedar bark in plain weave. The sides are wrapped, over slanting verticals and finer horizontals. A thick, three-strand braided handle is attached across the width. Collected by Edgar Dewdney in the late 19th or early 20th century.	L. 173	*Dewdney* 70/1927.9
27*	**Basket.** *Cedar bark, sedge.*	Nuu-chah-nulth nation. A flat-based, rectangular basket with a base of red cedar bark strips in plain weave. These strips are split to form the slanting verticals of the sides. The sides are wrapped over the verticals and the finer horizontals. Patterning of wrapped purple strips. Collected by Edgar Dewdney in the late 19th or early 20th century.	L. 122	*Dewdney* 70/1927.10
28*	**Basket.** *Cedar bark, sedge.*	Nuu-chah-nulth nation. A flat-based, straight-sided, rectangular basket. The base is red cedar bark strips in plain weave. The base strips are each split into two to form the verticals for the sides. The sides also are in plain weave using alternate wide and narrow weavers. Two rows of single-pair twining in sedge form the rim edge. Collected by Edgar Dewdney in the late 19th or early 20th century.	L. 70	*Dewdney* 70/1927.11
29*	**Basket.** *Cedar bark, sedge.*	Nuu-chah-nulth nation. A low, flat, circular basket. The centre of the base has a small central square of cedar bark plain weave, followed by twining and then wrapping which continues up the sides. Design of lines and spots in purple and dark blue. Collected by Edgar Dewdney in the late 19th or early 20th century.	Dia. 102	*Dewdney* 70/1927.12

*Illustrated

Cat No.	Name	Description of item	Size in mm	Collector/ Donor
30*	**Basket.** *Cedar bark, sedge.*	Nuu-chah-nulth nation. A flat-based rectangular, straight-sided basket. The base is of cedar bark checker-weave with one outer row of single-pair twining. The cedar bark strips are then split and turned vertically for the sides. The sides are in plain weave with two pattern bands near the base and just above the mid-line, of three green strips. Collected by Edgar Dewdney in the late 19th or early 20th century.	Dia. 102	*Dewdney* 70/1927.13
31*	**Basket.** *Vegetable fibre.*	Nuu-chah-nulth nation. A cylindrical basket with a flat base of closely set twining which continues up the sides for 6 rows. The sides then continue with alternate rows of a) plain weave, b) single-pair twining – three rows in red, three in brown – over pairs of verticals. At the rim are two close rows of single-pair twining and a row of braided stitching to hold the edge, the ends of the verticals being cut off very close. Collected by Edgar Dewdney in the late 19th or early 20th century.	Dia. 103	*Dewdney* 70/1927.14

*Illustrated

30

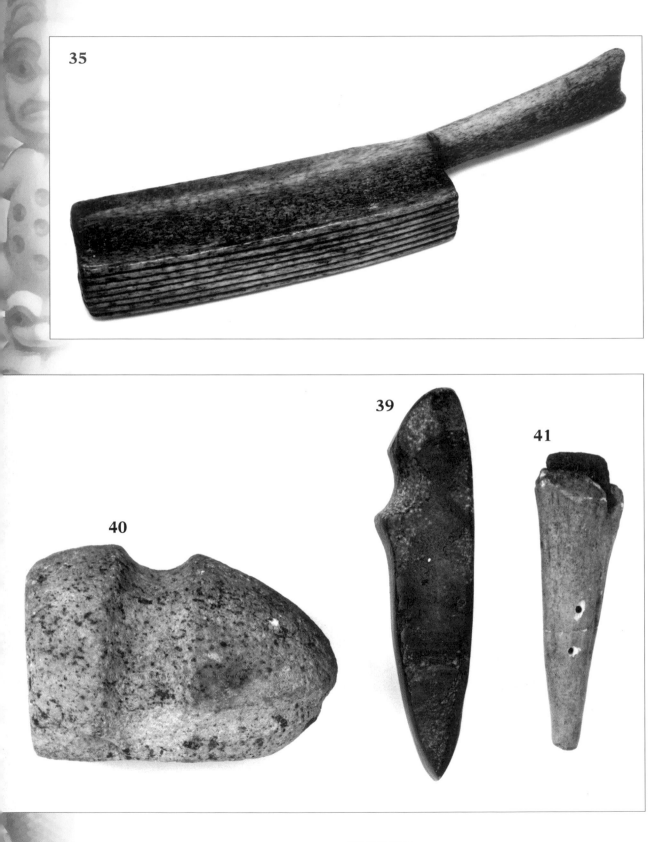

35

39

41

40

42

43

44

45

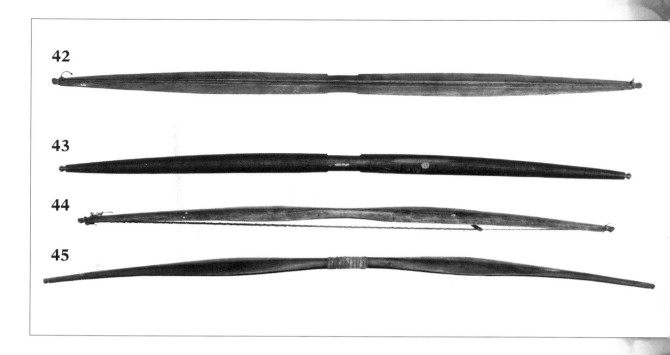

46

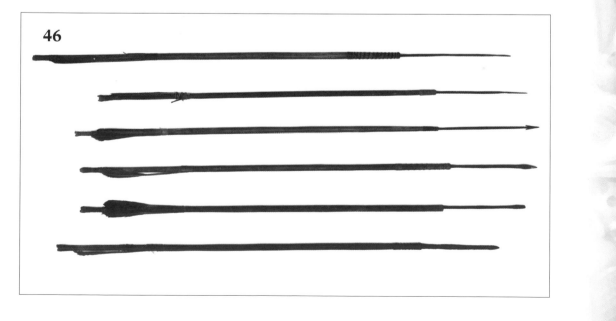

D: CLOTHING & PERSONAL ORNAMENT

Cat No.	Name	Description of item	Size in mm	Collector/ Donor
32*	**Labret.** *Wood.*	Haida or Tsimshian nation. A medial labret of oval shape. In the north labrets disappeared from use between 1805 and 1825. On the rest of the coast, south of the Tlingit territories, they were no longer in use by 1910 – 1920. Presented to the Devon and Exeter Institution in the early 19th century. Transferred to the Museum in 1869. Collected in the late 18th to early 19th century.	L. 78	*Devon and Exeter Institution* E1755
33*	**Cedar bark cloak.** *Yellow cedar bark, skin.*	Makah nation. Originally this garment was edged with sea otter fur that now remains only in fragments. Sea otter fur was reserved for the nobility. The borders are said to be woven with dog hair, although all tests carried out on cedar bark capes have revealed that no dog hair was used, although mountain goat hair was. The process of making a cedar bark cloak was the work of women, and began with a prayer to the spirit of the cedar tree to ask for its bark. A strip up to 30cm wide was pulled from the length of tree; the inner bark was then separated from the outer bark and the inner bark folded into a bundle, the sapwood to the inside. Several bundles were tied to a shoulder harness for carrying to the drying place. After air drying over a line, the bark was soaked and then pounded over a smooth stone with a bark beater (see number 35). When beaten to the softness required it was woven on a loom consisting of a rope attached to a crossbar between two uprights, the cloth worked from the top down, with spaced double rows of twining. Yellow cedar bark is stronger than that of the red cedar and considered superior. Cloaks made for high-ranking people were always made from yellow cedar bark. The cedar tree has always been revered as a generous provider by the people of the Northwest Coast, for its many and diverse uses. Accessions documentation records that this item was acquired at Cape Flattery, Washington State, USA. Collected on the voyage of HMS *America* in 1845.	W. 1760	*Agassiz* E 797
34*	**Clothing element.** *Leather, porcupine quill, sinew.*	Interior Athapaskan origin, perhaps Tanaina, traded to the Tlingit. A length of grey-black semi-tanned leather ornamented on one side with woven porcupine quill in a 'stepped mountain' pattern. This element of clothing would have been attached horizontally to a leather shirt in parallel with other strips of similar dimension. Donated to the Devon and Exeter Institution in the early 19th century, and labelled as originating from 'Otaheite' (Tahiti). Transferred to the Museum in 1872. Collected in the late 18th to early 19th century.	L. 960	*Devon and Exeter Institution* E 1772

*Illustrated

E: TOOLS & CARVING IMPLEMENTS

Cat No.	Name	Description of item	Size in mm	Collector/ Donor
35*	**Bark beater.** *Whale bone.*	Northwest Coast. Carved from a single piece of whale bone, this beater was used to beat the inner bark of cedar to separate layers of bark, and to soften the fibres. It was used at right angles to the lay of the fibre, over a large flat pebble or a similarly sturdy base. The style of this beater is common to all the Northwest Coast nations. Collected between 1863 and 1866.	L. 270	*Gregory* E 772
36*	**D-adze.** *Wood, vegetable fibre, iron.*	Nuu-chah-nulth nation. The figure on the handle has been identified as eagle or hawk. Research in the 1970s identified this adze as Nuu-chah-nulth. Further research in British Columbia in 1996 suggests that it is of Kwakwaka'wakw origin and from the Kingcome Inlet area. Collected on the 1776-80 Pacific voyage of Captain James Cook, this item was illustrated by Sarah Stone at the Leverian Museum before 1783. See Pearce, 1974, p.18, Force and Force, 1968, p.153 and Kaeppler, 1978, p.264.	L. 254	*Vaughan (ex Cook)* E 1232
37*	**D-adze.** *Wood, iron, vegetable fibre.*	Nuu-chah-nulth nation. A single cedar shaving remains preserved between the blade and handle of this adze. Collected between 1885 and 1889.	L. 235	*Dyson* 80/1931.133
38*	**Beaver-tooth gouges.** *Wood, beaver incisor, skin, sinew, fish bone or whisker, resin.*	Northwest Coast. Two carving tools, each made from a beaver incisor bound to a wooden handle with skin and 'S' ply sinew cordage. Fish bone or whisker protrudes slightly from the back of the binding on E1761a. This type of tool was common on the Northwest Coast and among a number of Alaskan Inuit groups, and the Ingalik and other Athapaskans. The sharp edge was used to carve and gouge grooves, the smooth back to polish wood, and the outer edge to sharpen knives. Transferred to the Museum from the Devon and Exeter Institution in 1872. Collected in the late 18th to early 19th century.	a) L. 164 b) L. 153	*Devon and Exeter Institution* E 1761a & b
39*	**Adze head.** *Stone.*	Northwest Coast. This adze head of grey-black stone is documented as having been found on Haida Gwaii (Queen Charlotte Islands), historically Haida territory. It is not known how Elgee obtained this and the two following items.	L. 195	*Elgee* 30/1948.1
40*	**Maul head.** *Stone.*	Northwest Coast. This heavy Northwest type maul head was excavated at Ogden Point, Victoria, British Columbia, which historically is in Salish territory. It has a flat face for a T-shaped handle and vertical as well as horizontal grooving for securing a lashing.	L. 145	*Elgee* 30/1948.2

*Illustrated

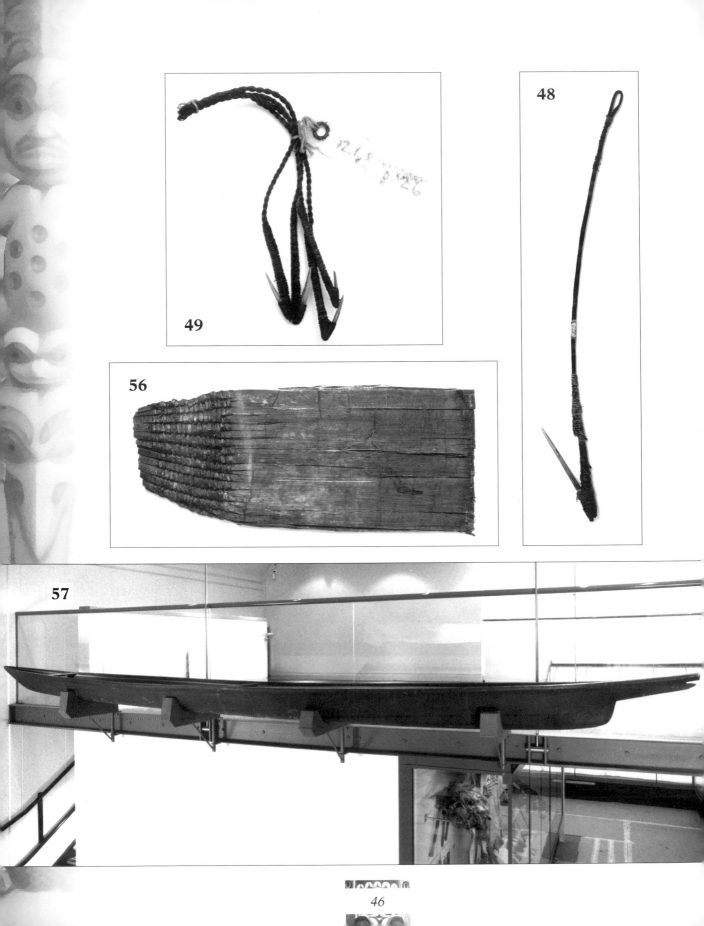

49

48

56

57

58

59

65

Cat No.	Name	Description of item	Size in mm	Collector/ Donor
41*	**Scraper.** *Bone or antler, iron, vegetable fibre.*	Northwest Coast. Originally accessioned as an adze, the size of this object suggests that it was more likely to have been used as a scraper. Vegetable fibre packing material is wedged around the iron blade where it fits into the handle. Collected at Ogden Point, Victoria, B C.	L. 56	*Elgee* 30/1948.3

F: FISHING, HUNTING & WARFARE

Cat No.	Name	Description of item	Size in mm	Collector/ Donor
42*	**Bow.** *Wood, sinew.*	Northwest Coast, Vancouver Island. Collected on Vancouver Island between 1863 and 1866.	L. 1250	*Gregory* E 773
43*	**Bow.** *Wood.*	Nuu-chah-nulth nation. Bowstring absent. Collected at Barclay Sound, Vancouver Island, between 1863 and 1866.	L. 1215	*Gregory* E 1670
44*	**Bow.** *Wood, sinew.*	Nuu-chah-nulth nation. Bow with bowstring of twisted sinew. Collected at Barclay Sound, Vancouver Island, between 1863 and 1866.	L. 1136	*Gregory* E 1671
45*	**Bow.** *Wood, hide.*	Nuu-chah-nulth nation. Bow with a medial ridge running down the outer face. Bowstring absent. Transferred to the Museum in 1872. Collected in the late 18th to early 19th century.	L. 1313	*Devon and Exeter Institution* E 1672
46*	**Arrows.** *Wood, metal, feathers, root skin, sinew.*	Northwest Coast, Vancouver Island. Six arrows, all with long metal fore-shafts. Collected on Vancouver Island between 1863 and 1866.	a) L. 743 b) L. 745 c) L. 767 d) L. 805 e) L. 721 f) L. 780	*Gregory* E 774 a - f
47	**Fish hooks.** *Wood, bone, bark, sinew, vegetable fibre.*	Northwest Coast, Vancouver Island. Three bent-wood fish hooks of a type in use until the 1950s in the southern and central areas of the Northwest Coast. These characteristic U-shaped, steam-bent 'halibut hooks' were also used for catching cod and dogfish. They were made from the hard, dense knot wood of fir or spruce. After each length was cut and shaped to the correct thickness, it was steamed and then bent using a mould of pairs of hardwood pegs driven into a cedar wood board in the shape of the hook. The barb was a splinter from the leg bone of a deer lashed on with a strip of split cedar or spruce root. Fishing and harpoon lines were made from twined nettle fibre, inner cedar bark, braided sinew and lengths of knotted kelp. Collected on Vancouver Island between 1863 and 1866.	a) L. 146 b) L. 141 c) L. 134	*Gregory* E 775 a - c

*Illustrated

Cat No.	Name	Description of item	Size in mm	Collector/ Donor
48*	**Fish-hook.** *Baleen, wood, sinew, bone.*	Northwest Coast, Vancouver Island. A jig-hook for cod and salmon. Jigging is a method of luring and catching a fish whereby the hook is jerked upwards at intervals on the end of a line in order to simulate the movement of its prey. Collected on Vancouver Island between 1863 and 1866.	L. 385	*Gregory* E 776
49*	**Fish-hooks.** *Wood, bone, nettle fibre.*	Northwest Coast. Bundle of 4 trolling hooks. Baited trolling hooks, attached to lines, attract fish by the way they move through the water when trailed behind a moving vessel. These slender, finely made hooks were used as a bundle. Collected between 1792 and 1794.	L. 88 (of bundle)	*Scott (ex Vancouver)* E 1268
50	**Fish-hook.** *Wood, bone, nettle fibre.*	Northwest Coast. A fish-hook for halibut, cod and dogfish. Collected before 1875.	L. 146	*Buckingham* E 1689
51*	**Fish-hook.** *Wood, bone, bark, nettle fibre.*	Northwest Coast. Collected between 1885 and 1889.	L. 160	*Dyson* 80/1931.140 80/1931.141 80/1931.143
52	**Fish-hook.**	Northwest Coast. Given to Canterbury Museum, Christchurch, New Zealand, 18 March 1948.	Unknown	*Dyson* 80/1931.142
53	**Harpoon heads and lines.** *Hide, bone or antler, iron, vegetable fibre, hair, gum.*	Makah nation. Two whaling harpoon heads and lines, both collected at Cape Flattery in Washington State, USA. E777b has tufts of black hair woven into the line, and an incised design on the barbs, mostly obscured by the binding. Both of these whaling harpoons (numbers 53 and 54) and the sealing harpoon (numbers 55) are items of cultural importance and considered to be sacred, and not to be touched or seen by women. For this reason they are not on display and photographs of them do not appear in this catalogue. Collected between 1863 and 1866.	a) Dia. of coiled line c. 280 - 320 b) Dia. of coiled line c. 450 - 540 L. of harpoon head 120	*Gregory* E 777a & b
54	**Harpoon head and line.**	Nuu-chah-nulth nation. This harpoon head and line were given to Canterbury Museum, Christchurch, New Zealand, in 1948. Collected at Nootka Sound in 1792 by James Woodward Scott.	Unknown	*Scott (ex Vancouver)* E 790
55	**Harpoon head and line.** *Bone, sinew, vegetable, fibre, bark.*	Northwest Coast. A harpoon head of two pieces of bone bound together in the centre with sinew to form barbs at one end and a notch to insert a blade at the other. The harpoon head is bound to a line made of vegetable fibre and then bound with narrow root strips. For hunting seal and porpoise. Collected on the 1776-80 Pacific voyage of Captain James Cook. Published in Pearce, 1976, p.19 and Kaeppler, 1978, p.275.	Dia. of coiled line c.700	*Vaughan (ex Cook)* E 1235

*Illustrated

67

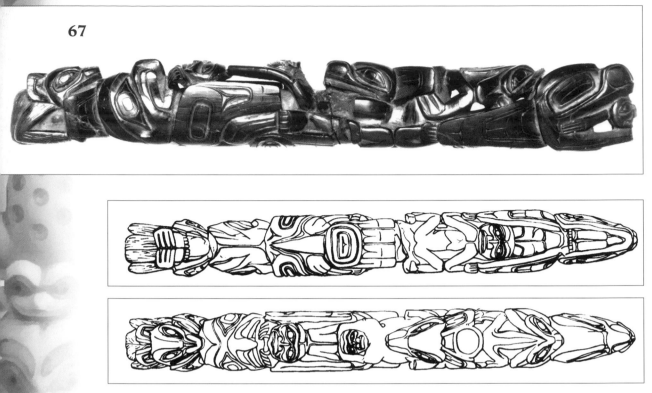

10. Crest pipe (see catalogue number 67).

68

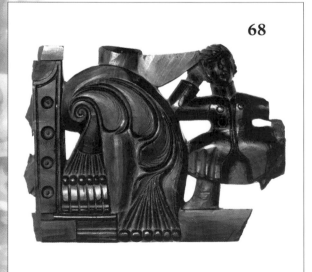

81

Cat No.	Name	Description of item	Size in mm	Collector/ Donor
56*	**Harpoon Cover.** *Cedar bark.*	Northwest Coast. This item was accessioned along with a 'barbed harpoon', which has not been identified in the collections. Collected between 1885 and 1889.	L. 307	*Dyson* 80/1931.144
57*	**Canoe:** *Sda'kwihl.* *Wood, metal.*	Coast Salish nation. Made from a single log, hollowed and shaped, this canoe shows evidence of having been hollowed out using a controlled burning method employing heated rocks. Further shaping was done with an elbow adze before a final steam-spreading to widen the beam for better stability. Collected by J D Agassiz in Klallam territory at Port Discovery, now Discovery Bay, Strait of Juan de Fuca, in 1845 on the voyage of HMS *America*.	L. 6400 (each)	*Agassiz* E 794
58*	**Canoe paddles.** *Wood.*	Salish nation. Two canoe paddles of wood, both with T-shaped handle butts. Collected by J D Agassiz in Klallam territory at Port Discovery, now Discovery Bay, Strait of Juan de Fuca, in 1845.	L. 630 (each)	*Agassiz* E 796a & b
59*	**Canoe paddles.** *Wood, pigment.*	Nuu-chah-nulth nation. The long, slender points of these small, light paddles ensured silence when the crew was approaching another canoe without wanting to be heard. They could also be used as spears when alongside an enemy boat. The painted design on two of the three paddles incorporates the head of an eagle. Presented to the Devon and Exeter Institution in the early 19th century. Transferred to the Museum in 1872. Collected in the late 18th to early 19th century.	a) L. 630 b) L. 759 c) L. 793	*Devon and Exeter Institution* E 1674a, b, c
60	**Canoe paddles.** *Wood.*	Northwest Coast. A canoe paddle with a T-shaped handle butt. Transferred to the Museum in 1974. Made in the mid to late 19th, or early 20th century.	L. 1795	*Weston-super-Mare Museum* 64/1974.60
61	**War axe, 'Slave killer'.** *Wood, hair, stone.*	Possibly Nuu-chah-nulth nation. This object was stolen from the museum in 1912. A description in the remarks column of the museum's Ethnography Register reads: *"Probably from Nootka Sound. The wooden handle carved into the resemblance of a face is ornamented with human hair – Native. ? Presume Taawisch or tsuskiah."* Collected on the 1776-80 Pacific voyage of Captain James Cook.	Unknown	*Vaughan (ex Cook)* E 1223
62*	**Whalebone club:** *Chitoolth.* *Whale bone.*	Nuu-chah-nulth nation. An early form of whalebone club. Collected on the 1776-80 Pacific voyage of Captain James Cook and illustrated by Sarah Stone at the Leverian Museum before 1783. Purchased by 'Vaughan of Devonshire' on the fifty-sixth day of the sale, it appears as Lot no.6614, 'war club, N. America' in the Sale Catalogue of 1806. See Force and Force, 1968, p.151. Published in Pearce, 1976, p. 17, Kaeppler, 1978, p.257.	L. 544	*Vaughan (ex Cook)* E 1222

*Illustrated

Cat No.	Name	Description of item	Size in mm	Collector/ Donor
63*	**Whalebone club:** *Chitoolth.* *Whale bone. abalone, hide.*	Nuu-chah-nulth nation. Collected at Nootka Sound. The head is carved in the form of the head of an eagle with an eagle head-dress. A leather thong runs through a hole drilled beneath the eye, and is knotted to form a loop for use as a wrist thong. Insets of abalone shell. This type of club was common all over the coast after contact with Europeans, and was traded into the interior regions of British Columbia. Collected between 1792 and 1794. Published in Gunther, 1962, p.99 and Pearce, 1976, p.59.	L. 507	*Scott (ex Vancouver)* E 1275
64*	**Whalebone club:** *Chitoolth.* *Whale bone.*	Haida nation. A club in the form of a salmon. Presented to the Devon and Exeter Institution in the early 19th century. Transferred to the Museum in 1872. Collected in the late 18th to early 19th century. Published in Gunther, 1962, p.99.	L. 549	*Devon and Exeter Institution* E 1733
65*	**Fish spear.** *Wood, metal, vegetable fibre.*	Nuu-chah-nulth nation. A long fishing spear with a wooden shaft and a metal point with two barbs. Most often used to spear smaller species of salmon. Collected at Barclay Sound, Vancouver Island, between 1863 and 1866.	L. 3390	*Gregory* E 1669
66	**Dart.** *Wood, vegetable fibre.*	Northwest Coast. This dart originally had a detachable point, now lost. Presented to the Devon and Exeter Institution in the early 19th century. Transferred to the Museum in 1872. Collected in the late 18th to early 19th century.	L. 340	*Devon and Exeter Institution* E 1677

G: EUROPEAN INFLUENCES & ITEMS PRODUCED FOR SALE OR TRADE

Cat No.	Name	Description of item	Size in mm	Collector/ Donor
67*	**Crest pipe.** *Argillite.*	Haida nation. Argillite, a soft, carbonaceous shale, is quarried at one site, near Skidegate on Haida Gwaii (Queen Charlotte Islands). Strict control of this site by the Haida means that all objects made from this material are by Haida artists. *Hlgas7agaa* is the Haida language word for argillite, in the Skidegate dialect. In spite of the central area of damage and loss, this is an extremely fine piece of carving, made without doubt by a master carver of the time. This carver would have employed his skills within his own society in the production of monumental works in wood such as totem poles, house posts and screens and mortuary poles, as well as masks and rattles for ceremonial use and smaller decorated items such as bowls, dishes and spoons. All items made from argillite were carved specifically for sale to Russian, American and European visitors to the region. Because of this there is no cultural meaning to the configuration of crest figures depicted: Killer whale, with a frog on its back, then wolf, hawk, small human figures, and wolf again at the mouth of the pipe. See Fig.6. This style of pipe was made by the Haida in the early 19th century.	L. 310	*Whitney* E 1265

Cat No.	Name	Description of item	Size in mm	Collector/ Donor
68*	**Panel pipe.** *Argillite.*	Haida nation. A section from a ship-panel pipe depicting a stylized tobacco leaf, two cascading bunches of tobacco berries, and a sailor who appears to be dancing. Argillite carving began as a commercial venture in the early years of the 19th century. It was acceptable to the ruling white population because it earned a cash income for the Haida without contributing to ceremonial practice. Haida artists were able to retain aspects of their culture at a time when it was under increasing threat. Made between the late 1830s when the Haida began to depict European imagery in argillite, and 1860 (Drew, 1980). Collection date and donor unknown.	L. 125	*Unknown* 163/1995
69*	**Model totem pole.** *Cedar pigment.*	Tlingit nation. This totem pole model was bought by Edgar Dewdney at the Indian School, Ketchikan, Alaska, June 25th 1914. It was made by Chief Johnson as a copy of his own full-size pole (Fig.7), carved in 1901 and now preserved in Ketchikan's Totem Heritage Centre. A replica made by the Tlingit carver Israel Shotridge was raised in 1989 on Ketchikan's waterfront. According to Rev. HP Corser, the author of *Totem Lore of the Alaska Indians (undated, published by the Ryus Drug Co., Ketchikan, Alaska* before 1917) the topmost figure is.... *......Kajuk, fabled bird of the mountains. This bird amuses himself by throwing rocks at groundhogs. Those who find one of these are sure to become very rich.* *Kajuk is placed high up to show the dignity of the family.* *Below are the two servants of the raven. These are the ones that obtained fire for mortals. The fire was in the west. These two servants stuck their bills into pitch and flew out to the fire. On their return the fire so heated the bill that under the weight of the burning pitch they bent, and the curve was produced. Below is the Raven, and still below is the fog woman with her children the salmon.* Comparison with the original pole (see Fig.7) shows that Chief Johnson shortened the height of the model considerably. This totem pole model and number 71 are important as they represent a period of degeneration of the art in the late 19th and early 20th centuries.	H. 518	*Dewdney* 70/1927.1

***Illustrated**

11. Chief Johnson's totem pole. This pole now stands in the Totem Heritage Centre at Ketchikan, Alaska (see catalogue number 69). (Photographer unknown.)

12. The totem pole at Kilisnu, Alaska, standing outside the Sun House (see catalogue number 70). (Photographer unknown.)

13. Ivory model of the totem pole at Kilisnu (see catalogue number 70).

Design "unwrapped" from the pole.

Cat No.	Name	Description of item	Size in mm	Collector/ Donor
70*	**Model totem pole.** *Ivory, bone, pigment.*	Tlingit nation. The original Kicksetti Tlingit totem pole, of which this is a model, stood outside the Sun house at Kilisnu, in the Stikine River region, Alaska, and is also illustrated in *Totem Lore of the Alaska Indians* (Fig.8). Made in two pieces, the painted pole is ivory and the base is bone. According to Corser, the figures, from the top, are: a face representing the mountain at Kicks Bay on the Stikine River that was the camping place of the Kicksetti in their migration north from the mouth of the Nass River; frog, emblem of the Kicksetti; Old Raven, the Creator, talking to young Raven that made man; Kilisnu beaver. See Fig.9 for the figural design 'unwrapped' from this model. "Top figure, human, wears *Yakwiwe* head-dress with ermine skins, used in *Tla-Sale* dance". Chief Adam Dick (hereditary chief, Kwakwaka'wakw nation), 1996. Made in the early 20th century.	H. 166	*Tilbury* 116/1967.2
71*	**Model totem pole.** *Cedar, pigment.*	Possibly Nuu-chah-nulth nation. The figures on this pole appear to be a human being and a bird, probably eagle. Flat back, rather than carved in the round. Made in the late 19th or early 20th century.	L. 382	*Bancroft* 114/1995
72*	**Spoon.** *Sheep horn, pigment.*	Tsimshian nation. The bowl of this spoon has been decorated in a European painting style and shows Northwest Coast topography of ocean, or inlet, mountains, islands and trees, with a steamboat in the foreground. The vessel was identified in 1996 by Bill McLennan, Projects Manager, Museum of Anthropology, University of British Columbia, and Leonard McCann, Curator Emeritus of the Vancouver Maritime Museum, as the Beaver, the first Hudson's Bay Company steamer to trade up and down the Northwest Coast. Collected at Skeena River, British Columbia. Made in the late 19th or early 20th century.	L. 246	*Wetherell* 43/1917.1
73*	**Model head canoe and four paddles.** *Wood, pigment.*	Northern Northwest Coast. Insensitive restoration of this boat model in this Museum in the past included remodelling and repainting of the bow and stern. The shape of the stern does not correspond to that of other head canoe models this author has seen, either published or in museum collections. The stern section may originally have been slightly shorter and 'cut-off' rather than rounded, but otherwise it is typical of the early to mid 19th century canoe design along the northern Northwest Coast. According to documentation at the time that these items were given to the Museum, they were collected at Hudson's Bay, Canada, in about 1836.	Canoe: L. 921 Paddles: L. 314 (all)	*Mrs Hannah Brushfield (ex Dr TN Brushfield) ex W Eales?)* 147/1911.1-5

*Illustrated

Cat No.	Name	Description of item	Size in mm	Collector/ Donor
74*	**Basketry-covered flask.** *Glass, sedges.*	Nuu-chah-nulth nation. A European glass flask, with two spherical bulges, covered in tightly twined sedge over slanting verticals on the outside and fine horizontals on the inside. On the middle square section of the flask there are vertical slats made by binding two warps together. Lidded. Collected by Edgar Dewdney in the late 19th or early 20th century.	H. 330	*Dewdney* 70/1927.16
75*	**Basketry-covered flask.** *Glass, sedges, cedar bark.*	Nuu-chah-nulth nation. A European glass flask covered in tightly twined sedge. Lidded. The open 3-way weave, in cedar bark, reveals the glass beneath the base swell of the flask. Collected by Edgar Dewdney in the late 19th or early 20th century. Published in Pearce, 1974, p.47.	H. 280	*Dewdney* 70/1927.17
76*	**Basketry-covered pickle jar.** *Glass, sedges.*	Makah nation. A basketry-covered European glass screw-top pickle jar. The base is in twined sedge and the sides are wrapped over a framework of cedar bark verticals on the outside and fine horizontals inside. The verticals rise at a slight angle, so that the wrapping slopes. Collected by Edgar Dewdney in the late 19th or early 20th century. Published in Pearce, 1974, p.47.	H. 140	*Dewdney* 70/1927.18
77*	**Basketry-covered flask.** *Glass, vegetable fibre.*	Nuu-chah-nulth nation. A European glass flask covered in twined vegetable fibre. The base is of four wide strips of the fibre which are then split to form narrower strips for the vertical elements. These rise at a slight angle. Lidded. Collected by Edgar Dewdney in the late 19th or early 20th century.	H. 162	*Dewdney* 70/1927.19
78*	**Basketry-covered jar.** *Glass, sedges.*	Nuu-chah-nulth nation. A European glass jar covered in very fine twining, including the base. The dark red-brown pattern on the sides is oversewn. The lid is also twined, with oversewn rings in pale, glossy cream–coloured fibre. A slender braided handle is attached to the jar. Collected by Edgar Dewdney in the late 19th or early 20th century. Listed in Pearce, 1974.	H. 42	*Dewdney* 70/1927.20

*Illustrated

Cat No.	Name	Description of item	Size in mm	Collector/ Donor
79*	**Totem Pole, Ilchinik.** *Red cedar, pigment, cedar bark (rope).*	Nuu-chah-nulth. Carved by Tim Paul, Master Carver; Patrick Amos, Francis Mark and Leslie Mickey, Senior Carvers; Tom Paul and Corey Baiden Amos, Apprentice Carvers. The figures on the pole were roughed out before it was shipped to Exeter from Vancouver Island and the pole was completed between June 6th and 24th 1998, in Rowley Gallery of this Museum.	H. 5 mtrs	*Commissioned*

Name and history from Hesquiaht and Ehattesaht groups, Nuu-chah-nulth nation:

The name of the pole is "Ilchinik". He was a very successful and powerful whaler.

The top figures:
Hu-pa-kwa-num - chief's box with all his wealth.
On the lid of the box is our Ha-witiisum sea chief.
The second figure is Ti-as.
This moon is Ti-as, our New Year. A new harvest season is beginning.
Hu-pat-moon is used as a very powerful symbol of preparation for our Hesquiaht, Ehattesaht people. We have 13 moons in our calendar.
Each month has a name which pertains to nature (such as) new greens growing, herring fish, berries, Fall, Winter.
Tu-tu-ch the elder Thunderbird. Thundering now and then.
Our people know Thunderbird has a home. Thunderbird lives in the mountains.
Thunderbird is so powerful, just lifting his wings a little makes everything tremble and shake below him.

Bottom figure:
Il-chinik the whaler was very successful at bringing in... whales with his many powers. He is a man who cleansed and prepared himself when the moon was growing. The fins of Whale are also the canoe of the whaler.
The back figure of the pole:
A very special race of people from out there. They left us with many good things. One thing was something which gave the ability to go anywhere we want in an instant and another was a powerful weapon, a round cylinder rock.

This totem pole celebrates the connections between Exeter and the Nuu-chah-nulth of Vancouver Island.
Na-yii-i family members, including elders and children who accompanied the carvers, were on hand in the carving gallery to answer visitors questions about Nuu-chah-nulth culture.
Ceremonial music, songs and dances were performed by all members of the Na-yii-i family, who are:
Chief Earl George and Josephine George.
Grace George.
Tim Paul and Monica Paul.
Tom Paul.
Corey Baiden Amos.
Patrick Amos.
Leslie Mickey.
Francis Mark and Mary Frank, William and Wilfred.
Linus Lucas and Donna Lucas, Justin, Jonsson, Lee and Kaytlen.
Darlene Amos, Andy Amos, Kerry Amos, Kimberly Amos, Krystle Amos and Peter Amos.
Virtual access to the project was available via a website set up by Telematics at the School of Education in the University of Exeter.
A 45 minute video has been edited down from some 25 hours of footage by film-maker John Sealey.
Sound recordings of ceremonies and presentations were also made as an audio archive.
A short film, a Living Elder, was made independently by Elmer Postle.

133/1998

Cat No.	Name	Description of item	Size in mm	Collector/ Donor
80*	**Painting.** *Paper, acrylic paint.*	Painting, *Chief's Box Killer Whale* by Tom Paul, signed and dated, June 20th 1998.	249 x 175	*Purchased* 151/1998
81*	**Carving.** *Cedar, acrylic paint.*	Carving of head of Raven by Krystle Amos. Made during the totem pole carving event, June 6th - 24th 1998.	L. 148	*Purchased* 154/1998
82	**Painting.** *Paper, acrylic paint.*	Painting of Whale by Patrick Amos, unsigned. Made during the totem pole carving event, June 6th – 24th 1998. Design for the Na-yii-i invitation to the dedication ceremony for Ilchinik (number 79).	250 x 250	*Patrick Amos* 154/1998
83	**Headband.** *Red cedar bark, raffia.*	Start of headband weaving, by Donna Lucas. Cedar bark brought from Vancouver Island by Na-yii-i family group, raffia purchased in Exeter. Made during the totem pole carving event, June 6th – 24th 1998.	L. 190	*Jane Burkinshaw* 255/1998
84	**Stencil.** *Paper.*	Cut-out stencil of wolf by Patrick Amos. Made during the totem pole carving event, June 6th – 24th 1998.	398 x 250	*Patrick Amos* 256/1998
85	**Sketch.** *Paper, graphite.*	Sketches on tracing paper, in pencil, by Patrick Amos of: c) Formline drawing of elements of human head (Nuu-chah-nulth) in profile. d) An eye form. e) An eyebrow form. Sketches made during the totem pole carving event and as part of workshop program.	300 x 164	*Patrick Amos* 257/1998
86	**Painting.** *Paper, acrylic paint.*	Painting of crow in flight by Peter Amos of the Na-yii-i family group signed, *Peter Amos, age 12, June 1998* and titled, *Crow*. Made during the totem pole carving event June 6th – 24th 1998.	420 x 297	*Peter Amos* 258/1998
87	**Carving.** *Red cedar, acrylic paint.*	Relief carving of head of wolf, in red cedar wood. Painted in black and red acrylic paint. Made during totem pole carving event June 6th – 24th 1998 by Peter Amos (age 12). Cedar brought from Vancouver Island by family group. Acrylic paint bought in Exeter. Signed on back, *WPA* and *Peter*.	L. 115	*Peter Amos* 258/1998

*Illustrated

Abbot, Donald N., ed.   *The World is as Sharp as a Knife:*
An Anthology in Honour of Wilson Duff
(Victoria: British Columbia Provincial Museum, 1981)

Abbott, Helen, et al., eds.   *The Spirit Within: Northwest Coast Art from the*
John H. Hauberg Collection
(New York: Rizzoli International Publications, Inc., 1995)

Allan, John   *'Artifacts at Exeter City Museums from Bligh's*
Second Voyage to Tahiti' (Pacific Arts, The Journal of the Pacific
Arts Association, Numbers 11 & 12 / July 1995)

Bancroft-Hunt, Norman,   *People of the Totem* (London: Orbis, 1979)
and Werner Forman

Bancroft-Hunt, Norman   *Native American Tribes* (Hertfordshire: Regency House, 1997)

Beaglehole, J. C., ed.   *The Journals of Captain James Cook on His Voyages of Discovery*
(Hakluyt Society: Cambridge University Press, 1967)

Beck, Mary   *Heroes and Heroines of Haida Myth and Legend*
(Alaska Northwest Books, 1989)

Beck, Mary Girando   *Potlatch: Native Ceremony and Myth on the Northwest Coast*
(Alaska Northwest Books, 1993)

Bruggmann, Maximilien   *Indians of the Northwest Coast.* (New York: Facts on File, 1989)
and Peter Gerber

Cameron, Anne   *Daughters of Copper Woman* (Vancouver: Press Gang, 1981)

Dzelarhons (Vancouver: Harbour, 1986)

Cole, Douglas   *An Iron Hand Upon the People: The Law Against the Potlatch*
and Ira Chaikin   *on the Northwest Coast* (Vancouver: Douglas & McIntyre, 1990)

Drew, Leslie   *Argillite, Art of the Haida*
(Vancouver: Hancock House Publishers Ltd., 1980)

Duff, Wilson   *Images stone B.C.: Thirty Centuries of Northwest Coast*
Indian Sculpture (Saanichton, B.C.: Hancock House, 1975)

Duff, Wilson   "The World is as Sharp as a Knife: Meaning in
Northwest Coast Art." In *The World is as Sharp as a Knife:*
An anthology in Honour of Wilson Duff Donald N Abbott, ed.
(Victoria: British Columbia Provincial Museum, 1981)

Fane, Diana,   *Objects of Myth and Memory: American Indian Art at the*
Ira Jacknis and Lise M. Breen   *Brooklyn Museum*
(Seattle: University of Washington Press, 1991)

Feest, Christian — *Native Arts of North America* (London: Thames and Hudson, 1980)

Fisher, Robin — *Vancouver's Voyage: Charting the Northwest Coast* (Vancouver: Douglas and McIntyre, 1992)

Fitzhugh, William W. and Aron Crowell — *Crossroads of Continents* (Washington D.C.: Smithsonian Institution Press, 1988)

Force, Roland W. and Maryanne Force — *Art and Artifacts of the 18th Century: Objects in the Leverian Museum As Painted by Sarah Stone* (Honolulu, Hawaii: Bishop Museum Press, 1968)

Erna Gunther — 'Northwest Coast Indian Art: An Exhibit at the Seattle World's Fair' (Fine Arts Pavilion, April 21 - Oct 21, 1962 Seattle, 1962)

Haberland, Wolfgang — *North America* 'Art of The World' series, Number XXIV (London: Methuen, 1968)

Holm, Bill — *Northwest Coast Indian Art: An Analysis of Form.* (Thomas Burke Memorial Washington State Museum Monograph, no.1.Seattle: University of Washington Press; Vancouver: Douglas & McIntyre, 1965)

Houstoun, Wallace — 'Journal and Letter Book of Wallace Houston R.N. 1852-1857' Unpublished MS held at the Royal British Columbia Archives and Records Service, Victoria, British Columbia, Canada.

Jonaitis, Aldona — *From the Land of the Totem Poles: The Northwest Coast Indian Art Collection at the American Museum of Natural History* (British Museum Publications, 1988)

Kaeppler, Adrienne L. — "Artificial Curiosities" An Exposition of Native Manufactures Collected on the Three Pacific Voyages of Captain James Cook, R.N. (Honolulu, Hawaii: Bernice Pauahi Bishop Museum Special Publication 65. Bishop Museum Press, 1978)

Keddie, Grant R. — 'The Use and Distribution of Labrets on the North Pacific Rim' *Syesis*, 14:59 - 80 (1981)

Kirk, Ruth — *Wisdom of the Elders: Native Tradition on the Northwest Coast* (Seattle: University of Washington Press in association with the Royal British Columbia Museum, 1986)

Kopper, Philip	*The Smithsonian Book of North American Indians* (Washington, D.C.: Smithsonian Books, 1986)
Lincoln, Leslie	*Coast Salish Canoes* (Seattle: The Center for Wooden Boats, 1991)
MacNair, Peter, Alan L. Hoover and Kevin Neary	*The Legacy: Continuing Traditions of Canadian Northwest Coast Indian Art* (Victoria: British Columbia Provincial Museum, 1980)
MacNair, Peter, Robert Joseph and Bruce Grenville	*Down from the Shimmering Sky: Masks of the Northwest Coast* (Vancouver: Douglas & McIntyre, 1998)
Moziño, José Mariano	*Noticias de Nutka: An Account of Nootka Sound in 1792* Iris H Wilson Engstrand, ed. (Seattle: University of Washington Press, 1991)
Neel, David	*Our Chiefs and Elders: Words and Photographs of Native Leaders* (Vancouver: University of British Columbia Press, 1992)
Pearce, Susan	*Redmen of North America: A Catalogue of the North American Indian Collections in the Exeter Museums and Art Gallery* (Exeter Museums, 1974)
	Towards the Pole: A Catalogue of the Eskimo Collections (Exeter Museums, 1976)
Reid, Bill, and Robert Bringhurst	*The Raven Steals the Light* (Vancouver: Douglas & McIntyre, 1984)
Stewart, Hilary	*Indian Fishing: Early Methods on the Northwest Coast* (Seattle and London: University of Washington Press; Vancouver/Toronto: Douglas & McIntyre, 1977)
	Looking at Indian Art on the Northwest Coast (Seattle and London: University of Washington Press; Vancouver/Toronto: Douglas & McIntyre, 1979)
	Cedar: Tree of Life to the Northwest Coast Indians (Seattle and London: University of Washington Press; Vancouver/Toronto: Douglas & McIntyre, 1984)
Taylor, Colin	*North American Indians* (Bristol: Parragon, 1997)
Vancouver, George	*A Voyage of Discovery to the North Pacific Ocean and Round the World, 1791-1795* W. Kaye Lamb, ed. (Hakluyt Society, University of Cambridge Press, 1984)

Waldman, Carl

Atlas of the North American Indian
(New York: Facts on File, 1985)

Walters, Anna Lee

The Spirit of Native America
(San Francisco: Chronicle Books, 1989)

Wardwell, Allen

*Tangible Visions: Northwest Coast Indian Shamanism
and its Art* (New York: The Monacelli Press, Inc., 1996)

Wright, Robin K.

A Time of Gathering: Native Heritage in Washington State
(Seattle: University of Washington Press, 1991)

Yenne, Bill

The Encyclopaedia of North American Indian Tribes
(London: Bison Books, 1986)

ACKNOWLEDGEMENTS

I would like to thank all those who have given of their time and expertise in sharing information that has contributed to this collections catalogue.

Particular thanks go to Kim Recalma-Clutesi, Potlatch Recorder, daughter of Kwakwaka'wakw hereditary chief Arnold Recalma and friend of many years, for her thoughtful contributions to my understanding of First Nations history and culture. I am also grateful to Kim, and to Kwakwaka'wakw hereditary chief Adam Dick for comments on likely origins of items and their cultural significance, and for providing Kwa'kwala language names.

Others deserving of thanks here are the late Alfred Recalma, the late Martha Recalma, and Bill Recalma of the Kwakwaka'wakw nation; hereditary chief Earl Maquinna George and Josephine George, Tim and Monica Paul, and the Na-yii-i family of the Nuu-chah-nulth nation; Wilfred Sampson, Gitksan-Tlingit nation; Herb Rice, Salish nation; Jerome Parnell, Haida nation.

At the Museum of Anthropology, University of British Columbia I want to extend thanks to Bill McLennan, Projects Manager and Lyle Wilson of the Haisla nation, Artist in Residence (1996). At the Vancouver Maritime Museum, Leonard McCann, Curator Emeritus. At the Vancouver Museum, Lynn Maranda, Collections Manager. At the Royal British Columbia Museum, Alan Hoover, Chief of Anthropological Collections and Grant Keddie, Curator of Anthropology. Thanks also to the staff of the British Columbia Archives and Records Service in Victoria, and to Jesse Petavel for her invaluable assistance with research there. Also to Phyllis and Wayne Taylor for access to their private library of publications on Northwest Coast arts and British Columbia history.

Colleagues at the Royal Albert Memorial Museum have also contributed to this catalogue, and I am grateful to Len Pole, Curator of Ethnography for his expert direction from the first to the final draft, and to John Allan, Curator of Antiquities for generously providing considerable information from his research into the history of the collections. Many thanks also to Veronica Johnston for technical advice on basketry methods, to Lucy MacKeith for proof-reading, comments on the text and general enthusiasm and to Graham Searle for his essential contribution of wit and wisdom.